To Veda, Jeff and Chris
for the strain
on their patience

Acknowledgments

It would not be practical to publish the complete list of those many
organizations and individuals who gave of their time and knowledge for
this book. However, the author does wish to extend his special thanks
to the following: Mr. Robert T. Howard, vice-president and general
manager, KNBC; Mr. James Parks; Dr. Tsaihwa J. Chow, Scripps Institute of Oceanography; Dr. John Phillips and Dr. Don Abbott, Hopkins
Marine Station; National Park Service, U.S. Department of Interior; Dr.
Clare Patterson, California Institute of Technology; Walter Thomsen,
California Department of Fish and Game; Mr. Harold Koenig, Ecologi-
cal Science Corporation; Mr. Doyle Grabarck, University of Maryland;
Institute of Marine Biology, Miami, Fla.; Florida Institute of Technol-
ogy, Mr. Richard Carter, JALEM Productions; Leigh Wiener
Photography; Mr. Louis Fuller, Los Angeles Air Pollution Control
District; Statewide Air Pollution Research Center, Riverside, Calif.; U.S.
Department of Health, Education and Welfare; and Milton Farber, Anti-
Pollution Corp. of America.

Foreword

Way back in 1969 A.D., Don Widener asked me to narrate a
television special he was writing and producing for KNBC-TV
in Hollywood.

The subject of the show was pollution, the title was
"The Slow Guillotine," and I've been glowing in the reflected
sunburn of his many well-deserved awards for the program
ever since. *

Now — in the spring of 1970 — I cling to a tentative
hope that the current, politically popular noises about
ecology and pollution will indeed be translated into meaningful action which will clean up our air, our water and our land.

As *Timetable for Disaster* excellently states, noise is a
poor substitute for action, and we do not (repeat not) have
much time. Facing this compelling fact, I'd like to repeat
here the words I fired at you at the tag of Widener's program:

"At a scientific conference held just last month it was

revealed that there are no baby pelicans along the Southern California coast this year. Pesticides have made the egg shells so thin they break before they hatch. It's the same with most birds of prey. Pollution has reached the point where there is little left to contaminate. It's now just a matter of degree. How much can we tolerate and still survive?

"And don't be misled by the fact that pollution doesn't kill with dramatic suddenness. Fatal is fatal, whether you are conked with a rock or nibbled to death by a duck!

"Science, engineering, government and industry seem more intent on intramural bickering than cooperation; and yet these elements must work together in harmony if we are going to salvage the country from the mess that some feel is already irreversible.

"It sounds hokey, but you — the individual citizen — you are the only guy with a solution. You alone hold the power to move government and industry.

"Now we have shown you tonight how your resources are being plundered — year after year after year after year, and this while the government talks of studies to determine 'criteria' and 'levels of tolerance.'

"Science keeps trying to devise a tree that will grow in polluted air. Now for crying out loud, why do we have to put up with that?! And meanwhile, back at the factory, industry pleads for tolerance because purification equipment costs money.

"Well it's enough!

"Now, write to your congressman, the governor, or the mayor, and don't ask; *demand* action! Tell them what you saw on this program and if you get a form letter back, send a copy to his political opponent and keep one for yourself. You should know his name on election day.

"And, if you don't take over, pollution will; because at this point, it looks very much like Chicken Little was right."

— Jack Lemmon

*

The Alfred I. duPont — Columbia University Broadcast Journalism Award for Investigative Journalism

The Emmy — National Academy of Television Arts and Sciences (Station Award)

The Emmy — National Academy of Television Arts and Sciences (Hollywood Chapter)

Silver Award — International Film and TV Festival of New York

"Sci" Award — California Museum Foundation

CONTENTS

Aviation, Not Alligators

...And Furthermore

Timetable for Disaster

The Slow Guillotine

Suggested Readings

Introduction

I have always greatly admired those writers who can take on subjects of great importance and give them a hard-eyed analysis, somehow remaining objective and emotionally detached. Because I never have found the knack for that sort of thing, this is a book of essays — which is to say that in addition to the facts, my thoughts, opinions, and beliefs have infiltrated the text.

On the subject of pollution, which I have been worrying about for five years, I confess about as much emotional aloofness as Jack the Ripper at a Miss America pageant. If I appear to be an alarmist, it just happens I am running along here scared stiff. I have talked with perfectly rational men in the science fields who unblinkingly give this planet little more than fifty years as a suitable habitat for humans. Some men claim this is pure bunk, and the odds are 100 to 1 against such theories being true. Perhaps. I, for one, don't like the odds.

In the past couple of years we have come full circle, ecologically. From obscurity, concern for the environment has blossomed to become the number one topic in the land. Yet, as this is being written, we already hear people talk of being "bored" with the subject. Television critics complain of too many programs on the subject. This is rather remarkable in that throughout the world, the situation has only worsened.

There also is inexplicable confidence on the part of many government officials and some scientists. On a recent trip through western Europe and the United States, this became very obvious. What was not obvious was the reason for this cheerful outlook.

In England, I found scientists who seemed sure things were not as serious as we Americans seemed to believe — at least in the British Isles. Alex Hendry of the London *Times*, with a team of reporters, recently found a different story. *The Times* reported millions of tons of coal waste still being dumped into the sea. Twenty-three "dark towns" in England are still wrapped in a shroud of coal smoke and dust because their officials refuse to clean up the situation, as had been done in some other places. *The Times* found several rivers in England to be little more than cesspools, deoxygenated and virtually void of acquatic life.

In Sweden and Finland, we found the same curious belief that Europe is solving the problem, but the U.S. is in trouble. The gentle hint is that America has been backward about doing anything, and our scientists don't know as much about the subject as do the Europeans. This argument would have been more acceptable if any of the countries we visited had been able to master the art of properly frying an egg.

The facts do not seem to support the optimism we found in Europe. The Baltic Sea is a prime example. Already plagued by DDT, mercury, raw sewage, and a host of industrial pollutants being spewed from Denmark, Russia, Sweden, Poland, Finland, East and West Germany, the Baltic has now been determined to contain H_2S (hydrogen sulfide gas). It has been found in the Landsort Deep, the deepest part of the Baltic. A recent report by the International Council for the Exploration of the Sea (Cooperative Research Report, Series A, No. 15) notes: "If this development continues in the Baltic deep water, the whole water mass below the halocline will probably turn into a lifeless 'oceanic desert' such as is found in the Black Sea."

In the United States, government officials are prone to ooze confidence about the pollution situation. However, anyone who believes this should stand on the bank of the Hudson River in New York City and watch, as raw, totally untreated sewage comes gushing out. It's a real eye-opener and sinus-closer. However, some people still fish there. One fellow remarked: "I don't mind the fish; but I hate cleaning that stuff off my line."

Doubters would do well to stand on a trash dump situated on a bluff above the Youngstown, Ohio, U.S. Steel plant and just watch. It's an artist's delight. Black smoke, blue smoke, white smoke and even orange smoke. For those who say this is necessary and unavoidable, they should take a look at the Los Angeles basin on any day. No smoke from anywhere by anybody. The Youngstown U.S. Steel plant wouldn't last long enough in Los Angeles to manufacture a carpet tack.

In Cleveland, Ohio, I walked on a beach beyond a sign

which declared it safe and open for bathing. There were rotting tree limbs, old tires, and scum, along with an unidentifiable odor. In Washington, D.C., I watched a rat swimming up the tidal basin beneath a sign which warned not to fish there. The fish are contaminated. The rat had the scene all to himself — which may be prophetic.

The concern of this book, then, is the raw deal we have been handing Mother Nature for longer than anyone can remember, and the sobering fact that she is finally beginning to even the score. As many thoughtful men have been trying to tell us for some time, we are in trouble — deep trouble. *How* deep is anybody's guess. Every day there are new data to bolster their theory that we have blundered very close to the chasm of ecological disaster. There are those among these men of science who fear we are no more than a generation or so from extinction for the human race, unless total war is waged against pollution — now. There are men of equal stature who believe the danger from pollution is grossly exaggerated and we are in no way threatened. They are honest in their conviction. So, I believe, was the captain of the Titanic, who held that there "are no icebergs this far south."

D.W.
Northridge, California

TIMETABLE
FOR DISASTER

DDT:
The Benevolent
Executioner

It was in 1948 that the Nobel prize for medicine went to
Swiss chemist Dr. Paul Mueller. At the time, it certainly
seemed few men in history had been so deserving of the great
honor. It was Dr. Mueller who had discovered the almost
magical power of DDT, a whitish crystalline substance with
fantastic power to kill insects without apparent harm to
humans. First formulated in Germany in 1874, DDT's termination talents were hidden until Dr. Mueller brought them to
light. Since that time the material has been credited with
saving millions of lives by curbing insect-borne diseases such
as typhus and malaria.

Following the war, DDT was happily embraced by
farmers, foresters, and millions of backyard botanists. Here
was a compound effective against a vast array of insects. As
growers dumped DDT on their fields in ever-increasing
amounts, forestry officials used it to spray everything from

spruce budworm to the gypsy moth, and housewives came to accept the dust as the ultimate solution for anything with wing or feeler.

Meanwhile, in laboratories across the country, researchers probed every aspect of DDT in hundreds of experiments. Its effect was checked on land and sea – and on everything that could walk, swim or fly. The blizzard of paper reports that resulted were often confusing, frequently ominous, and gave the first indication that the newly hatched bluebird of happiness might be growing up as a vulture.

Many scientists who had suffered pangs of conscience ever since DDT was introduced now began to recall Dr. Mueller's cautioning that little was known about possible side effects of DDT. By the time the 1950s had dawned, some began to express concern. "Supersubstance" was beginning to exhibit disturbing traits.

In 1962, the smoke broke into open flame with the publication of Rachel Carson's now famous book *Silent Spring,* which exposed publicly for the first time the schizoid nature of DDT. She nailed the compound dead center, detailing its persistence in our environment and its blindly indiscriminate lethality. Its portent for mankind was dramatically pictured in her vision of a world stripped of wildlife – even the songbirds.

In flogging DDT, Miss Carson undoubtedly struck a noble blow for humanity; however, she had, at the same time, dared to smite the darling of the chemical-agricultural combine, which to that point had been marching in happy lockstep unobstructed by a knowledgable public. Picking up her girlish gauntlet and gathering their pesticidal petards, the farmacological forces mounted a counter-offensive, hurling rhetorical shot and shell upon the enemy. Miss Carson, said they, was callously indifferent to the humanitarian role of DDT. On top of that, they sniffed, she hadn't the proper "scientific credentials," and in the main, added to nothing more than a nutty little old lady "bird-watcher."

While many chemists of commerce were picturing DDT as scarcely more dangerous to man than ice-cream topping, spokesmen for agriculture were describing the terrors of a world unprotected by the pesticide. The visions conjured were of muscled, ravenous insects marching through America's farmland and devouring everything except brand name tractors and 4-H members. During this period of stress for government and industry, not much was made of the fact that our nation — by great good luck or spiritual intervention — had managed for generations to survive the hordes of hummers. No matter; the danger was clear and present: without DDT we were in for mastication massacre by the little devils.

The attack against Miss Carson was so severe, the outrage of her opponents so complete, one would have thought the poor lady had mugged Santa on the way to the orphanage. She remained undaunted, however, and slugged it out with her detractors toe-to-toe until her death two years later. It is one of the inequities of life that we often cannot survive to see the effect of our works. Such was the lot of Miss Carson. Had she remained awhile, she would have enjoyed knowing that she had proved, after all, more effective against *her* pests than the DDT users had theirs.

Today, eight years after *Silent Spring,* Miss Carson has succeeded, in absentia, in shooting the pesticide posse from their saddles. The death rattle for DDT could be heard as the 1960s faded, with Health, Education and Welfare Secretary Robert Finch announcing a two-year phaseout of all but "essential uses" of the compound. It can be assumed that Secretary Finch has similar plans for the other "hard" pesticides, and that it will become not merely a ban of use but of manufacture as well. The necessity for this will become clear, later in this chapter.

So be it. At long last, the governmental leaders are awakening to the danger of DDT. The rennaisance, however, is somewhat tardy and raises a nasty question. Why has it taken local, state and federal governments so long to move when Miss Carson exposed the culprit almost a decade ago, and research reports were readily available well before that?

The Department of Agriculture has doggedly defended the hard pesticides since their inception, and in so doing has had a most friendly association with chemical concerns which manufacture and sell such products. This kindredship, born of common aims, managed to keep DDT pipelines unclogged, despite mounting evidence of important side effects and growing dissent from scientists and laymen alike.

This unseemly "togetherness" of the USDA and the chemical interests eventually attracted the watchful eye of the House Committee on Government Operations, which in the fall of 1969 delivered a sharp cuff to the Agriculture Department for that agency's refusal to heed reports from HEW concerning dangerous levels of pesticide residues in human food.

In its report, the committee charged that the USDA's Pesticide Regulation Division (PRD) ignored HEW findings and warnings in approving the registration of almost two hundred pesticide products. The committee also plowed into USDA for failing to initiate even one criminal suit over a period of more than a decade "despite evidence of repeated violations by some shippers." Conflict of interest, as common as cocktail parties in Washington, also came up in the committee report. Specific cases were mentioned, involving Shell Chemical Company. In one instance, a PRD official left his government job to accept a position with Shell. In another, a Shell executive was appointed by Secretary of Agriculture Orville Freeman (1965) to aid PRD in its studies of criteria to be used in determining whether to grant approval of registration for pesticide products.

The committee's report, of course, strongly implied the USDA-chemical industry relationship was, like DDT, too effective and long lasting. It is a better explanation for the pesticide's charmed existence than the more common plea that the government has not had firm evidence of the material's damage potential.

It is not difficult to find *some* support, even for the most idiotic of theories. There are, for instance, a few souls who still flatly deny the world is round, Apollo be damned. Therefore, it is in no way surprising that DDT has retained a strong base of support within government and industry — long after the fires of logic have been scattered and dampened. There are, today, government officials and industrial chemists who speak, hear, and see no evil in the continued use of DDT, a curious stance in light of known facts about the pesticide.

Since the first day science slipped the leash from DDT,

it has been wildly, irrevocably beyond the control of man.
This unhappy fact of life is a consequence of the same char-
acteristics that got Frankenstein a D in citizenship: a refusal
to "die" after a decent interval, and a penchant for showing
up where not invited.

Let's take the matter of longevity. Backers of DDT are
fond of estimates that give the substance a "half-life" of ten
years. That means the stuff should lose half its potency
during that period. That would be bad enough, were it true,
but it probably isn't. The figure is based on wishful thinking,
and at any rate would be an average, inasmuch as DDT
"breaks down" at varying rates under varying conditions. The
ten-year guesstimate is unsubstantiated by any worthwhile
evidence. As a matter of fact, nobody knows for sure just
how long DDT will keep its vigor.

One biologist I talked with about the pesticide shrugs
off any attempt to establish an accurate "life" for DDT.
"Who the hell knows? My own guess would be perhaps fifty
years, but it could be ninety or a hundred. But, I'd bet on
one thing: all of it ever used is still going strong."

Of course, it is DDT's super life-span that makes it both
a boon and bane for the world. To growers, it means a fatter
money belt. For the insect problem DDT is the chemical
coup de grâce. While it isn't as toxic as some (a couple of
drops of certain pesticides on your skin can prove fatal) it
sticks around to do its killing for a long, long time. One shot
does the trick, whereas other types of pesticides may "break
down" to harmless ingredients within a few days or weeks.
On the farm there is a direct translation into extra dollars —
dollars saved in time, labor, and the cost of the pesticide

itself. If DDT or other long-lasting poison is not used, then it is necessary to spray more often to achieve the same result. This, in turn, means higher cost for the farmer, which results in higher cost for the consumer.

A nomad by nature, DDT moves with the abandon of a hippie with a credit card. It is difficult to apply the material with accuracy. It has been estimated that a crop-dusting airplane is lucky to dump half its load on target. The rest drifts away on the wind, settling where it will. Once released, DDT starts on the move. Part of it evaporates with water from the soil. Some leaches through the soil, reaches underground water, and eventually finds its way to a river or stream. DDT is often applied, accidently or by design, directly to bodies of water. Once in the air or water, DDT molecules attach to particles of matter there — dust, for example. The ultimate repository for DDT are the oceans and seas. It comes in the rain, in runoff from streams, and from dust, sifting down from the skies. Ocean currents distribute it around the globe.

Because DDT is dispatched with such efficiency to all areas of the world, a ban on *use* and not on the *manufacture and sale* of the substance borders on the ridiculous. A farmer spraying DDT in Italy sprays the West Indies as well, for the insecticide can drift there within days. Ditto a grower in California, who can contaminate countryside thousands of miles away. Since roughly 80 percent of all DDT manufactured here is sold for export to other nations, banning the *use* in the continental U.S. is in violation of the ancient admonition against spitting into a high wind. We will have exchanged our shotgun for a biochemical boomerang.

Today, DDT is as ubiquitous as bill collectors. There isn't a spot on our planet so remote that one could go there and not find a colony of pesticides in residence. Penguins in the Antarctic carry DDT residues in their flesh, despite the fact that DDT has never been used in or near the Antarctic.

Since DDT is virtually insoluble in water, it hangs around in the oceans with the persistency of an out-of-work nephew. However, while it resists breaking down in water, it exhibits an unfortunate affinity for oil or fat, in which it readily dissolves. This is a rotten break, since almost every marine organism has oil or fat in its system, in varying amounts. Such organisms represent home sweet home for DDT, which moves in and settles down for the duration.

The DDT which accumulates in marine life is found even in plankton, the microscopic plants and animals that grow in stupendous numbers in the oceans of the world. Plankton, which get their name from a Greek word meaning "wandering," drift with the currents or swim weakly. Phytoplankton (plant) and zooplankton (animal) both contain oil, absorb and retain DDT, and serve as major food sources for fish and other marine creatures. As the plankton is consumed, the DDT is passed along and added to the pesticide residues already existing within the fish. Small fish are devoured by larger fish, which are in turn eaten by still larger fish, and so on up the marine "food chain." At each step, the pesticide residue builds up progressively, in a process called *biological magnification.* Thus, science has discovered, marine inhabitants carry concentrations of DDT much higher than that existing in their environment. For example, while ocean water contains DDT measuring a few parts per *trillion,* DDT in the fatty tissues of larger fish is counted in the many parts per *million*.

The tiny amount of DDT in the oceans (in comparison to the volume of water) is a favorite point of the public relations drum and bugle corps of the pesticide forces. They maintain the substance is found in such minute quantities it is difficult even to trace. True. However, they follow this fact with an assumption which is not: since there is so little, it can't be meaningful. It can, and it is.

At the end of the marine food chain are to be found the fish-eating birds and animals. The heavy residues of DDT in the fish they consume are passed on to these hapless creatures. The effect on birds, such as the brown pelican, the bald eagle (America's national symbol), the peregrine falcon, the osprey, and the Bermuda petrel, to name a few, has been disastrous. All are facing extinction.

Most often, DDT strikes at the source of life, interfering with the reproductive mechanism by destroying the mother bird's ability to produce sufficient calcium. Her eggs, as a result, have thin shells, often nothing more than a membrane. Consequently the eggs are crushed in the nest by the mother's weight.

The rare and graceful Bermuda petrel is one such victim. Believed extinct until a few years ago when some were discovered near Bermuda, the petrels have not escaped the pesticide menace even though they live far at sea, nesting on barren outcroppings of rock. They love food high in oil and fat — and subsequently high in DDT. Since the late 1950s the survival rate of the petrel young has dropped drastically. It is feared that the species will become simply a memory — a picture in an encyclopedia — by 1980.

Peregrine falcons, the swift and strong hunters prized by the nobility of the Middle Ages, when falconry was a favored sport, also are counted among the losers to DDT. They have been obliterated as a nesting population in the eastern United States, and they are in deep trouble in California, their egg shells growing thinner each year.

As for the brown pelican, the hero of story and verse, it is making its last stand on the Pacific coast of America. In 1969, only two baby pelicans were reported to have hatched. Investigations by Dr. Robert W. Risebrough of the Institute of Marine Resources at the University of California in Berkeley confirmed the perilous plight of these birds. On Anacapa Island, off the coast of Southern California, he found empty nests, or nests with crushed eggs.

The pelicans once nested by the thousands along the California shoreline. It now seems inevitable that they must pass from the scene, as they already have in Lousiana — ironically known as the Pelican State — and in Texas. In these regions, the pelican thrived before the advent of DDT. In the 1940s the pesticide plague came, the DDT running off from farmlands and washing down the Mississippi River to the Gulf. Within a few years, the pelicans were gone. Now facing extinction in their remaining habitats, there is scant reason to expect them to return to the Louisiana-Texas coast . . . or to any other site, for that matter.

Sometimes, the DDT residue in a fish can be so high it is immediately injurious to a bird that eats it. This happened recently to a bald eagle, which became paralyzed on the spot. Generally, however, the eagle is affected in the same manner

A PELICAN EGG on the California coast. DDT is used widely in California.

END OF THE LINE is ahead for the pelican, along with most fish-eating birds. The comic pelican, favorite of children, is succumbing to DDT. This fellow is the only baby of the species found on the Southern California coast in 1969.

as the pelican. Both the eagle and the mighty condor appear to be on the list of the condemned among the wildlife.

And what is the effect upon the staunch supporter of DDT. Does it pluck at his heart strings to think of the ecological disaster in process? Does it summon a lump of sympathy to his throat? Does it, in fact, even register? It would seem not. Even when it is admitted that DDT can kill wildlife, it has an overtone of chance, as though the happening were accidental and isolated. As one scientist put it, in defense of DDT: "DDT has undoubedly killed birds . . . for example, robins that got in the way of the nozzle when elm trees were being sprayed to control Dutch elm disease."

On the basis of that statement, we are asked to believe that wildlife need only step to the rear of the sprayer to assure their survival. Assuming, then, that all the pelicans, eagles, falcons, condors and such now being wiped out have somehow unerringly perches in front of nozzles, there remains a puzzle. How in the hell did they get a spray nozzle two thousand miles into the Atlantic to get at the petrels? Truly a scientific achievement.

Of course, for the cynical among us, it seems at least remotely possible that the above remark could have been the result of commerial blindness or alarming ignorance . . . although admittedly, the two are not mutually exclusive. The "robins and nozzles" theory might have been more acceptable in the 1940s, when little was known about DDTs effects. By the early 1950s any scientist familiar with DDT and its long-lasting cousins should have been able to sense the coming disaster. Treatment with DDT at one pound per acre for control of spruce budworm in Maine during 1954 resulted in heavy fish kills. In Illinois during 1959, there was heavy loss of wildlife, and birds were virtually eliminated during a one-week period following the application of dieldrin at three pounds per acre to control Japanese beetle. Aldrin, used in Michigan (1959-61) for Japanese beetle control, killed an estimated thirty-eight thousand wild animals and birds. In 1964, Paris, Tennessee got a dose of dieldrin during an aerial spraying to control white-fringed beetle. There was, of course, widespread mortality among wildlife. Fish, pigeons, songbirds, rabbits, squirrels — all died, along with a variety of insects. A city water-supply tank was contaminated, but the poison was luckily discovered before water was released into the municipal system. Rightfully indignant citizens held a protest meeting and the "treatment" was stopped.

There are many hundreds of such reports, detailing the results of using DDT or other "hard" pesticides. Time and again, the data have pointed to the same conclusion: such pesticides cause vast damage, immediate and long range. For some reason, this handwriting on the wall, loud and legible years ago, has been ignored by the USDA. *Why* remains to be determined. The House subcommittee may have uncovered even more than it realizes.

At any rate, the heat must have been getting a trifle high in 1969, because the USDA finally announced it was cutting back on use of DDT and the other long-lasting pesticides in cooperative federal-state programs, as in the spraying of national forests. On the heels of that decision came another one. It would reduce the use of these substances at civilian airports, but not at military airfields.

Interestingly enough, the USDA said it was taking the action in reducing the use of hard pesticides to offer greater protection to wildlife, and to lessen the danger of soil contamination. It is interesting because Dr. George Irving, administrator of the Agricultural Research Service, was saying about the same time that DDT registration could not be cancelled until the pesticide was proven unsafe or ineffective. He said no evidence had been found to support either.

It would seem overwhelmingly evident that the use of the hard pesticides is unsafe — dangerous for all forms of wildlife, and possibly humans as well. DDT's effectiveness is not above question, either. It has failed to eradicate a single pest, although it has made about a hundred fifty species immune to it. It's an old and familiar story. Insects are tremendously adaptable and resilient. The first application of DDT may get almost 100 percent of a given species. The next year that same species will lose fewer of its population to the poison, and the next year even fewer, as it develops its resistance.

England found out about DDT's ineffectiveness in the summer of 1969, when London suffered a garbage strike. As the garbage piled up, Londoners found themselves locked in battle with "superflies" which proved immune to the hard pesticides, including DDT.

And what about man? What is the pesticide's effect on him? Information is sketchy, but what *is* known has given medical scientists cause for concern. The effect of exposure to heavy amounts of DDT is well known; the symptoms being watery eyes, profuse sweating, blurred vision, and diarrhea. A really large dose will cause trouble in breathing, turn the skin an odd purple color, and possibly reduce the victim to a coma. However, few persons have ingested enough DDT to cause these effects.

There are other potentially dangerous, long-range possibilities. DDT is a cumulative poison which will dissolve in the fatty tissues of people and animals and stay there, like a genie in a bottle, waiting to get out. This fat is actually reserve energy which can be summoned when needed. In a bird, for example, it can happen on a long migratory flight. As the regular supply of fat (energy) is expended, the reserve comes into play. At that point, DDT trapped in the fat tissues is released and pumped directly into the body system through the blood stream. The sudden infusion of poison can be lethal.

Today, scientists are wondering. Does the same situation apply for humans? When an obese person undergoes a rapid weight loss, as in a crash diet, will the resulting transfer of DDT from the excess fat to the blood system cause illness or even death? We simply don't know. Perhaps there will be no effect; people are not birds. On the other hand, we know that the human body's reaction to many drugs and chemicals changes in the presence of DDT. For instance, the liver's metabolic activities are different when its cells are exposed to the pesticide. It is known that cancer can be induced in mice by application of a large dose of DDT.

There is no way to predict DDT's long-range effects on man. We are reduced to dangerous and futile speculation. Because we failed to heed our own findings many years ago, a discontinuation of DDT now still leaves the world soaked in the substance, which will go on working for decades to come. For better, or probably for worse, we are wed. One thing

seems certain, whatever the changes DDT brings about in
man's system: they will not be for the better.

One reason for the USDA action in finally putting the
brakes on DDT was the newly found courage of the nation's
scientists — or at least some of them. Normally a retiring lot,
they have come out in increasing numbers to join those
seeking a ban on the hard pesticides. In May 1969, a large
group of marine scientists in California, under the leadership
of Dr. John H. Phillips, Jr., director of Hopkins Marine
Station of Stanford University, warned of the dangers of
pesticides in an open letter to Governor Ronald Reagan. The
letter was signed by sixty-two Ph. D. scientists, representing
Hopkins, Scripps Institute of Oceanography, Moss Landing
Marine Laboratory, California Institute of Technology, San
Francisco State College, the University of California at Santa
Barbara, the University of California at Santa Cruz, Bodega
Bay Marine Laboratory, the California Academy of Sciences,
the Pacific Biomedical Research Laboratory of the University
of Hawaii, Pacific Marine Station of the University of the
Pacific, the University of California at Irvine, Sonoma State
College, Hartnell College at Salinas, the University of Califor-
nia at Los Angeles, and the Naval Postgraduate School at
Monterey.

In their statement, the scientists concluded that "the
scientific evidence now available shows beyond question that
DDT and its residues have caused serious and irreparable
damage to populations of beneficial birds and fishes." They
strongly urged, at the conclusion of their letter, that further
use of DDT be banned.

While California, the country's biggest user of DDT,

dragged its political/agricultural feet, along with the USDA, some other states and nations took action. Michigan put a stop to DDT in a hurry when several tons of coho salmon from Lake Michigan had to be confiscated because they contained DDT residues well above the legal limit. Arizona, in 1969, slapped a one-year moratorium on DDT because the pesticide residue in milk might make the state's dairy products unsalable.

In Sweden, DDT and other chlorinated hydrocarbons such as lindane and dieldrin were banned when the Swedes discovered to their horror that the Baltic Sea was so infested with DDT that certain fish from those waters were unsafe to eat on a regular basis. Denmark promptly followed suit, outlawing the pesticides in the fall of 1969. Neighboring Finland and Norway approved the move by the Swedes and Danes and are expected to ban hard pesticides shortly.

All the problems are not with fish and milk. In 1968, several tons of lettuce being shipped east from Salinas, California, "the lettuce capital of the world," was ordered destroyed after Food and Drug Administration checks showed a DDT concentration of 9.1 parts per million (ppm) — 2.1 ppm above the maximum permitted by law. A year later, the USDA (slow learners) ruled that both toxaphene and DDT could be used during early growing periods, but could not be applied to lettuce and cabbage after the heads form, when the plants are nearing maturity. Officials said the ban was instituted to prevent build-up of pesticide residues.

The latest state to be wounded economically by the pesticides was Arkansas, which discovered as Thanksgiving neared that it had less than usual to be thankful for. A large

THIS IS A TREE IN WASHINGTON, D.C., our nation's capital. Lots of things happen at night in Washington, including the spraying of trees. Congress meets in the daytime.

helping of the 1969 Arkansas turkey crop had been pre-
stuffed, right on the ranch. With pesticides. A lot more than
the law allows. The luckless gobblers went the way of the
coho salmon and Salinas lettuce. It was enough to make one
doubt the validity of claims about how much money pesticides save the farmers. In the long run, higher-priced food
may be a better bargain than no food at all.

Meanwhile, if all the above hasn't roused the concern of
our leaders, there is a dandy problem lurking in the oceans —
quite removed from the one we already have with our fish. In
a quiet little two-page research paper, "DDT Reduces Photosynthesis by Marine Phytoplankton," published in *Science*
(March 29, 1968), Dr. Charles F. Wurster of the Department
of Biological Services, State University of New York, may
have given man a peek at doomsday.

Dr. Wurster's paper relates findings from his study of
the effects of DDT (a few parts per billion in water) on
photosynthesis by marine phytoplankton. The phytoplankton,
as mentioned previously, are the microscopic plants that
serve as food for many creatures of the sea. They also perform another valued service. They manufacture approximately 70 percent of the earth's supply of oxygen, without
which man promptly expires.

Dr. Wurster's research revealed that DDT can reduce the
phytoplankton's ability to produce oxygen, and concluded
that this inhibition "may be of ecological importance." At
the time his paper was published, Dr. Wurster made it clear
that very little is known about the effect of DDT on phytoplankton, and added ominously: "Since a substantial portion
of the world's photosynthesis is performed by phytoplank-

ton, interference with this process could be important to the biosphere."

You bet your sweet bippy, Doctor.

The work by Dr. Wurster was performed in a laboratory. His experiments utilized water with DDT concentrations higher than those found in natural sea water. However, it is known that phytoplankton accumulate DDT to a point where they contain a much higher concentration than is found in their environment. Will the phytoplankton in the ocean eventually be affected as were those in Dr. Wurster's laboratory? In his report, Dr. Wurster writes: "Evaluation of the significance of these findings to phytoplankton communities in nature is not simple, although the near-ubiquity of DDT residues implies a potential for widespread effects."

On the whole, it may be that Miss Carson underplayed her hand. We could eventually have not only silent springs, but inaudible summers and winters as well. Due credit for this pitiful prospect must be granted to the chemical companies and their willing partners, the agricultural interests — both mesmerized by their P and L (profit and loss) statements. Afflicted with target fixation in pursuit of their commercial carrot, they seem unaware that mindless pursuit of P may deliver the ultimate L.

The chemists seem to have taught the USDA their ancient parlor game in which they find something tall to leap from and no fair peeking. It's an interesting enough game because you don't know the ending. It works out equally well for pill, potion, or pesticide. Mix up a few ingredients, add assumptions, and voilà! A new product. Register and distribute. Sometimes it works, other times (thalidomide,

DDT) it doesn't.

In the case of DDT, the chemists made a bush league play. They forgot to check their -*cidal,* which has turned out more *sui* than *pesti.*

Running Scared

In the years before the Second World War, the cold, blue waters of the Pacific off the Northern California coast were the envy of fishermen the world over. Great schools of sardine swarmed there, out from the majestic Monterey Peninsula, and the catches were legendary, sometimes reaching 800,000 tons in a single year.

In the waning years of the war, the hauls began to diminish. By 1947, the annual take had slipped to 150,000 tons. The fishermen were not worried, they knew the reason: too many sardines had been taken. The fish would return. They always came back. Their optimism was rewarded with an upsurge the following year, and by 1950 the take was 400,000 tons.

In 1951, the giant fishery completely collapsed. It simply vanished. The sardines made minor gains in sporadic peaks on statistical charts, but by the beginning of the 1960s,

only traces remained of the once-mighty fishery. California
fish and wildlife experts credited the sardine disappearance to
overfishing, a familiar happening. The fish would eventually
make a comeback.

One man, a water-quality biologist working for the
Department of Fish and Game at Terminal Island in Los
Angeles, noticed something odd in the pattern of the decline
of the sardines. Walter Thomsen, experienced in entomology,
saw a distrubing irregularity: the survival ratio of young fish
was abnormal. When an adult fish population declines, nature
compensates with an *increase* in the survival percentage of
the offspring. In the instance of the Pacific Coast sardines,
the reverse had occurred.

To Thomsen, the variant stuck in his mind like a red
warning flag. *Something* out of the ordinary was happening,
and that something nagged at him incessantly. Finally, on a
hunch, he checked in at the library and began to comb agricultural books, looking for latest figures on the amount of
the long-lasting pesticide DDT being used in California. What
he found added muscle to the hunch. DDT, introduced in the
1940s had been used in steadily increasing amounts. Now, in
1963, it was being dumped on California's farm fields at a
rate of thirty-five million pounds per year.

Armed with the new data and the annual figures for the
sardine catch during the same period, Thomsen plotted both
on a chart. The result was chilling. The sardine population
declined in almost perfect ratio to the escalation in the use of
DDT!

The concerned Thomsen pondered the possibilities. Did
it mean anything? Could there be a viable relationship? Ob-

viously, overfishing was a major factor in the sardine decline, but what about the failure of the young fish to increase? Could the pesticide be a contributing cause, or perhaps even the principal reason?

"At the time," recalls Thomsen, "the idea was fantastic. "No one believed DDT could have such effects. Still it bothered me. The water run-off patterns would carry DDT from agricultural areas into the oceans at the very point where the sardines were most abundant.

"Most of the people I talked to thought the whole thing was a big joke, but I decided to send my chart to our headquarters in Sacramento, anyway. I guess when they saw it, they got scared the theory might get out to the public. One fellow later told me that the first man who saw it jumped to his feet and started running down the hall, waving the chart and yelling 'Oh, no! Oh, no!' "

Shortly afterward, according to Thomsen, he was warned not to talk with anyone about his findings, and he was ordered to stop all work on the study.

"I told my superior that he would have to put that order in writing," said Thomsen, "because I had been hired to work on water pollution, and I felt the matter might be important and serious, and should be investigated further. I got the order to stop. In writing."

Thomsen said he reminded his superior that if the hypothesis turned out to be true, and a hearing were held one day, it might be awkward to have been the person signing that stop order. "He told me that he wasn't worried, because everyone knew it was *his* superior that had passed the order down to *him.*"

MAJOR AGRICULTURAL AREAS OF
CALIFORNIA AND WATER RUNOFF PATTERN

SAN FRANCISCO

MONTEREY

OCEAN AREAS RECEIVING MAJOR RUNOFF
COINCIDE WITH AREAS OF
INITIAL SARDINE DECLINE

Thomsen expects to "make waves" with his decision to finally permit this story to be told. "I suppose I'll get my knuckles rapped, but I feel it is important that this kind of information be placed before the public. At the time of the stop order, I was told 'someone else is working on the project.' That was not true, some were working on the sardine decline and others were studying DDT . . . but nobody was examining the possibility that DDT was a factor in that decline."

Thomsen lists eight reasons for believing his theory may be true.

1. The correlation of sardine catch and DDT is technically an "inverse correlation."
2. Large agricultural runoff puts DDT in the sardine area.
3. The initial decline occurred where the runoff enters the ocean.
4. DDT is known to be highly toxic to fish and fish food-organisms.
5. DDT is known to be accumulating in ocean fish throughout the world, including sardines and even open-ocean tuna, which have been found to contain up to 300 ppm DDT in their oils.
6. DDT has a known capability to stop the reproduction of fish. An example is the Lake George, New York case, where normal-appearing lake trout (adult) could not reproduce because of DDT they contained. Their young died at the completion of absorption of the yolk sac, when DDT concentration was above 2.73 ppm.
7. The survival ratio of young sardines went down during the decline of the school, as mentioned above.
8. Because sardines are oily fish, they accumulate DDT faster than some other fish. DDT is insoluble in water, but highly soluable in fat or oil.

Thomsen admits his data "do not prove cause and effect," but points out that "they do sustantially support the hypothesis. Obviously, correlations can be fortuitous. One might correlate with light bulk production, or units of furniture . . . but these do not accumulate in fish tissues, are not highly toxic to fish in trace amounts, do not have the run-off pattern, et cetera. Critics who use the argument that correlations may be accidental have a poor case in this instance."

According to Thomsen, one biologist examined that data with the idea of "ruling it out" as a hypothesis. "He couldn't do it," said Thomsen. "I seriously wonder if the amount of data supporting this hypotheses could occur by chance alone."

Thomsen's theory, fantastic as it must have appeared in 1963, is not looked upon as so implausible in the decade of the seventies. In his article "DDT: Boon to Man or Bane to Air Environment," *Washington Post,* May 4, 1969, Dr. Wurster (see DDT: The Benevolent Executioner) cautioned that our fisheries may be in jeopardy. Said Dr. Wurster: "The implication is clear. The failure of trout and salmon to produce fry [their young] in Lake George and Lake Michigan may soon be repeated among some of the world's major marine fisheries, if it is not already occuring. Some commercial species have indeed shown sharp and unexplained declines during recent years. The prospect is hardly reassuring for those who look to the sea for the increased food supply required by an increasing number of human mouths."

Dr. Wurster is joined in his concern by many marine biologists, who see the possibility of collapsing fisheries as even more worrisome than the chance the phytoplankton

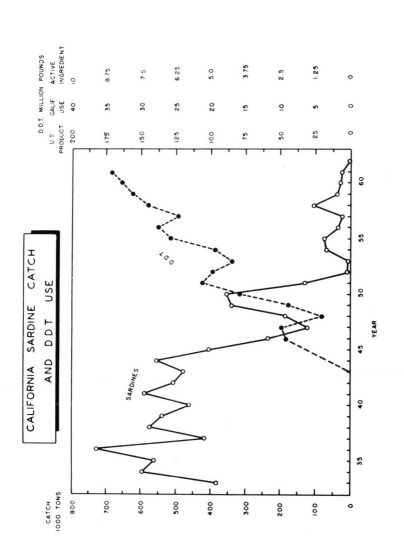

CALIFORNIA SARDINE CATCH AND D.D.T. USE

may one day cease to provide us with oxygen. Their point is
that the loss of great schools of fish may be an imminent
event, while the demise of the plankton is probably not. The
picture of a world without a ready supply of fish is not a
pretty one in the face of an increasing population and an
already inadequate food supply. Widespread famine, with all
it portends, would seem inevitable.

Such warnings, if they are heard and understood by
governments of the world, are apparently disbelieved. There
is no move afoot at this time to ban the manufacture and use
of hard pesticides. Talk is of "phaseout" and use for only "critical needs and crops." Meantime, the pesticides are poured on
the land and waters to join the huge concentrations already
there.

The ubiquity of pesticide residues in the oceans and in
marine life cannot be denied. It is doubtful one could find
fish anywhere on the globe that are free of the substance. In
a recent independent sampling of fish (canned) selected from
a grocery shelf, a testing laboratory analysis showed the
following:

Mackerel (Japanese)	DDE	. . . . .0.42 ppm
Crown Prince Brand	DDD	. . . . .1.1 ppm
Sardines (Maine)	DDE	. . . . .0.21 ppm
Beach Cliff Brand	DDD	. . . . .0.26 ppm
	DDT	. . . . .0.62 ppm
Star-Kist Tuna	DDE	. . . . .0.18 ppm
	DDD	. . . . .0.10 ppm

Pink Salmon	DDE	. . . . .0.07 ppm
Peter Pan Brand	DDT	. . . . .0.30 ppm
	DDD	. . . . .0.13 ppm

I selected the above cans of fish at random. There is little doubt that *any* brand of *any* fish would have contained similar concentrations of pesticide residues. The laboratory analysis was on the fat basis. To check fresh fish, I purchased several samples at a fish market at Redondo Beach, California. The results were similar to the above figures, although concentrations ran slightly higher. The fish were local, having been caught off the Southern California coast.

We may be creating damage of which we are not even aware — or do not understand — through the spread of pesticides. The chances are very good that enormously important changes have been made in the ecological balance of our planet. Some are already public record; some are only now surfacing; and others undoubtedly are in process, to be discovered after the fact.

A good case in point is the population explosion of a once-rare sea creature called the crown of thorns starfish. For some reason, which baffles and worries marine scientists, the crown of thorns have become so abundant during the past decade that they are threatening to tilt the ecological scales in their ocean communities. Normally, according to marine biologists, the crown of thorns is held in check because only a few survive from every million eggs produced by the mother starfish. The rest are devoured by other sea creatures that are their natural predators.

However, it is not the number of starfish that bothers marine biologists; it is their activity. The starfish eat coral reefs. They are dining on those reefs protecting Hawaii's high-priced beaches as this is being written. They have destroyed a hundred square miles of the Great Barrier Reef of Australia, and have polished off nearly all the coral surrounding Guam. Because the reefs protect beaches and small islands they are extremely important. Without reefs, the surf can pound in unimpeded and even wash away small, low-lying atolls. Reefs are also important food sources for islanders, since fish congregate in and around the coral.

Why have starfish colonies suddenly mushroomed? Scientists throughout the Pacific area are searching for an answer, but as yet there is none. However, Walter Thomsen ventures a theory: the same pesticides responsible for the

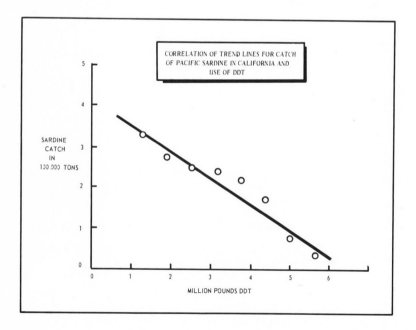

CORRELATION OF TREND LINES FOR CATCH OF PACIFIC SARDINE IN CALIFORNIA AND USE OF DDT

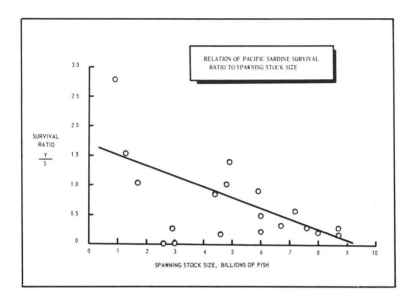

RELATION OF PACIFIC SARDINE SURVIVAL RATIO TO SPAWNING STOCK SIZE

SPAWNING STOCK SIZE, BILLIONS OF FISH

collapse of the California sardine fishery may be at the root of the starfish situation.

Thomsen believes the long-lasting pesticides could have killed off sea creatures that feed on the starfish young and allow only a few to reach adult size. Without natural predator control, says Thomsen, it would be reasonable to expect the starfish to multiply. There is an interesting coincidence to Thomsen's theory. The starfish problem was first noted in Australia in 1963 — the same year Thomsen noticed the correlation between the decline of the sardines and the rise in the use of DDT.

If Thomsen's thinking proves correct, perhaps it will move a few more of us to think about the possible effect before we spring something new on Mother Nature. As Robert Ingersoll once remarked: "In nature there are neither rewards nor punishments, there are consequences."

The overabundance of starfish is a *consequence.* It may be a consequence of our use of DDT, or the result of something else. But it has long been the generally unheeded plaint of the ecologists that the rest of us have never grasped the simple rule of nature; that if we disturb it *here,* there will be a following reaction *there,* which in turn will create another reaction, and so on.

Those who understand this rule are careful to emphasize that not all of man's disruptions of nature are bad — some can be beneficial. Man can build and progress, providing he gives proper consideration to his environment in the process. Unfortunately, he seldom does. In the use of DDT, too few gave a hoot in hell about the effect on environment, if, indeed, they ever thought about it one way or the other.

It will be morbidly interesting to follow the starfish story, to trace the total effect as far as possible. Certainly there will be obvious deleterious results from the destruction of coral reefs. Beaches will be unprotected, some low-lying atolls may simply wash away. Fishing will probably deteriorate in important areas. If Thomsen's theory works out, it poses an additional question: What happens to the creatures that lived on the predators that consumed the young starfish, and so forth? It is a domino pattern that must follow any break in the ecological web.

As data mounts regarding the effect of pesticides on marine life, it becomes increasingly clear that the demise of the sardines and the proliferation of starfish are not isolated incidents of ecological disruption. The crab harvest in San Francisco, once a hefty nine million pounds annually, has

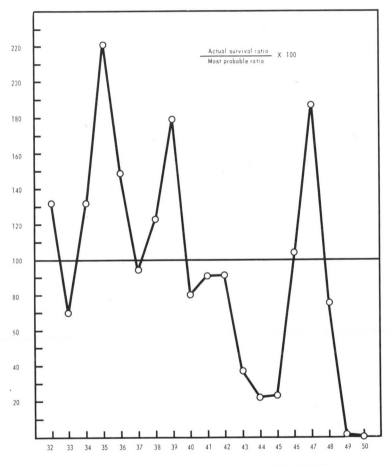

$$\frac{\text{Actual survival ratio}}{\text{Most probable ratio}} \times 100$$

PACIFIC SARDINE SURVIVAL RATIO AS PERCENT OF MOST PROBABLE RATIO.

dropped steadily over the past decade, and now stands at one
million pounds or less. Research indicated DDT is at fault,
killing off the crab larvae before they can hatch.

Government action against the contaminants may be
considerably too late, and much too little, for the reasons
mentioned previously: the long life of the pesticides, and the
fact that the vast majority is still to be exported, from
whence it can return.

NOWHERE TO GO — Hardpressed by pesticides and encroaching civilization,
a flight of birds wheels over Cuthbert Lake, Everglades National Park . . .
where they almost lost out to a huge jetport planned for construction — an
act that would have destroyed the park.

If Thomsen's 1963 theory proves correct, and if, as he states, there was no similar work being conducted when he was ordered to cease his study, then the Department of Fish and Game in California should be asked some pertinent questions. Why was Thomsen told to stop? Why was he told to refrain from talking about his work? If the order came from higher up, then how high? Was Thomsen duplicating others' work? If not, why was he given that story?

These questions and more become important because Thomsen's findings, if true, should have resulted in an immediate halt to the use of pesticides such as DDT. If Thomsen was halted because of political pressure applied on behalf of DDT interests, we should know it. If true, we have blown seven years coming to grips with the problem. And that's bad luck.

Smog:
The Killer Veil

Pretty funny stuff, air. It's invisible. You can't smell it or taste it, but you can weigh it, expand it, compress it, freeze it — even transform it to a liquid. Chemically, it breaks down to about 79 percent nitrogen, 19 percent oxygen, with the remaining 1 percent composed of water vapor, argon, krypton, neon and such.

Plants manufacture it, animals and people breathe it. Nature uses it to absorb the sun's heat on the one hand, and to reduce the amount of heat radiating away from the earth on the other. Man has found many ways of harnessing it for his own needs; for example, in the operation of air-driven (pneumatic) equipment.

Air is by far the most important substance supporting the continuance of life on earth. If you doubt this, try holding your breath for two minutes. Five minutes without air and we die.

Admittedly, this is all pretty obvious, and probably academic. There is no shortage — at this time. However, don't get comfy about it. We are not in a position of oversupply. Our air is sufficient, but finite. It surrounds the earth like the skin of an apple, extending upward only a few thousand feet. At an altitude of two miles, cars cease to function well and so do people, simply because the oxygen is beginning to thin out.

Since there is universal agreement that air is of paramount importance, surpassing even money and girls, it is reasonable to assume that man, in this golden age of science, would long ago have taken the steps necessary to insure the continuity and wholesomeness of this marvelous substance. But has he? Of course not! He has, instead, made its elimination a possibility and its contamination an established fact. Having done this, in the name of progress, profits, prosperity, politics, and proliferation, there is now going to be hell to pay . . . and the first bills have come due.

Our statement that man could forfeit his oxygen supply as a function of his own advancing technology will, I suppose, be attacked by some of the scientific community. Be that as it may, the possibility (if not probability) of a reduced air supply exists.

Let us peruse a "theoretical possibility" that has matured to hard fact: widespread and dangerous air pollution. Once thought of as a "nuisance" and passed off somewhat unscientifically as merely "smoke," air pollution is finally being recognized — somewhat tardily — as a complex problem and a deadly threat to all living things.

One would think, from the confusion created by its

arrival in Los Angeles in the early 1940s, that smog slipped in during the night with the stealth of a Sikh sentry. Actually, smog has been around longer than a late, late movie. Few punches have been telegraphed as far in advance as was air pollution. Even the Spaniard Juan Cabrillo, sailing in California's San Pedro Bay back in 1542, took note of it, naming the place La Bahia de las Fumas (the Bay of Smokes) in his diary. At that point in time, the problem was one of too many Indian campfires. It was about four hundred years before we understood what Cabrillo was trying to tell us.

Historians are usually forgiving of those who stumble in the face of new and previously unknown challenges. I recall that the Roman general Scipio got a fair shake in the record books, even though he was trounced on a sucker play by Hannibal. But then, it can be fairly asked, how many generals had ever been confronted by an alpine elephant army?

In our national failure to recognize the approach and calculate the seriousness of air pollution, we have frittered away our big chance for sympathy from the upcoming generations. There are no "outs." We blew it. There were warnings, plenty of them, but the world had other things on its mind. When Belgium's Meuse Valley was hit by a murderous fog, laced with pollutants from industry, who noticed? It was 1930, and the market had collapsed. We were busy chasing bankers who had decamped out the back door with large sacks.

We got a second notice in 1948, this time from Donora, Pennsylvania. It was late in October, when a stagnant air mass descended on Donora's 14,000 inhabitants like a dirty sheet. Foul air was not alien to Donora, with its wall-to-wall in-

SOMEWHERE UNDER THERE IS NEW YORK CITY,
which once laughed at Los Angeles' smog.

dustry, but the residents had never seen anything like this. Sealed by an inversion layer, the town steeped in a brew of pollutants that would otherwise have dissipated. On the sixth day it rained, the smog lifted, and Donora took stock. Of the city's population, 6000 had become ill, 20 had died. The story took a back seat to the red-hot battle for the Presidency between Harry Truman and Thomas Dewey.

London, England, upped the ante in 1952 when it was socked in by an inversion, heavy fog, and the inevitable build-up of pollutants from industry and coal-heated homes. When the skies cleared, less than a week later, the grim statistics were revealed. The death rate had soared far above normal. About four thousand above!

If the rest of the United States was deaf, dumb, and blind to the lesson of London, officials in one city — Los Angeles — sat up and paid attention. The city, rounding out its first decade of fuming, fumbling, and frustration as the smog capital of the nation, was finally beginning to crack the formula of air pollution; to understand the scope of its problem. With understanding came respect and concern — even fear. What had started as a pussycat problem with simple solutions (it was announced at a 1943 mayors' conference that smog would be "entirely eliminated" within four months) had turned into a tiger that eluded the best scientific know-how that could be brought to bear.

It was pointed out earlier in this chapter that we got off the starting blocks several decades late in the race against atmospheric pollution. But at least Los Angeles got into the race after it spotted the opponent. The rest of the country looked at the Southern California plight and laughed. Smog

was ridiculous. Even the *sound* of it was funny. Besides, the
rest of the nation could finally jest about the Californians'
climate, instead of the other way around. The shoe was on
the other foot. What they hadn't noticed was that the foot
was in their mouth. Smog was about to prove it didn't play
favorites. America was to find out that it owed those long-
suffering, eye-smarting Angelenos a debt.

As the U.S. Department of Health, Education, and
Welfare pointed out in a recent report on the federal air
pollution program (*Public Health Service Publication No.
1560,* Revised October 1967), "the experience of Los
Angeles helped to demonstrate that a new and more complex
air pollution problem was emerging, for as they began their
control efforts, officials in Los Angeles found themselves
faced with many technical problems that could not be solved
through the traditional methods of smoke abatement. One of
the results was that citizens of a single county were soon
supporting a research effort needed not just in Los Angeles
but for the entire country."

It was not until 1955 that Congress got around to
passing legislation designed to come to grips with the mounting
threat of air pollution. It could hardly have delayed longer, in
the face of massive data which said Trouble Ahead in neon.

If the federal government was a slow learner, it had
plenty of company. Cities and towns throughout America
believed (and many still do, apparently) that smog "can't
happen here." This cheerful belief is one of a raft of fairy-tale
misconceptions extant in the land concerning smog and other
forms of pollution and their effect on our environment.
Officials of such cities are placing their citizens in the posi-

LOS ANGELES — Smog

. . . and more smog

tion of receiving their protection from the same source as the
working girl: Heaven. It seems unlikely that this colorful
theory will prove any more successful for the one than it has
for the other. In fact, the antipollution programs of these
towns could be prosecuted just as effectively by having each
resident deposit a bowl of milk and two cookies on his door-
step and depend on the gnomes for surcease.

Some cities, and a few foreign powers (including the
Soviet Union), wisely and aptly concluded years ago that Los
Angeles County was not being put upon by some selectively
vengeful god. What was happening to Southern California,
they reasoned, could happen anywhere as population and industry continued to expand. They came to California to
watch and study at the source.

As a training ground, a farm club for smog fighters, Los
Angeles has been unparalleled. Through careful observance, a
junior smogman may become expert in not only the chemical
recipes of air pollution and the techniques and equipment
required for its reduction or elimination, but in the political
guerilla tactics often required to convert know-how to ac-
complishment.

The ultimate smog warrior is a being of diverse
talents and traits. He is sort of the Green Beret of Glop, able
to mix molecules with the chemists, play clerk and dagger
with politicians, and perform as Wyatt Earp among the polluters. There aren't many, but Los Angeles has one — Air Pollution Control District Officer Louis Fuller. A tough former
police officer, Fuller is honest, intelligent, likeable, mean
when he must be, and, as many have discovered, doesn't
corrupt worth a damn. It is not an easy job. Controlling and

cajoling the pro and con forces in the smog arena has been compared to the role of hand-feeder in a piranha hatchery.

In the years ahead, the job of air pollution officers will become easier because of the experience and data mined in Los Angeles. It was a long, bumpy road which has led Los Angeles to where it stands today, a city that can boast of the cleanest, best-controlled industrial base in the world. If you want to test that statement, climb up on a hill and look over the City of the Angels. Try and spot a single plume from a stack. Zero.

Not that it went that smoothly or nobly. It didn't. There were false starts, dumb proposals ("Let's bore holes in the mountains and let it out into the desert!"), and an unwillingness to make a serious pass at the mighty auto manufacturers. Smog officials went after the easy game first, knocking down citrus grove smudge pots, backyard burners, and industrial incinerators. Later, it worked up enough muscle to take on the bigger "stationary sources" — the power plants, oil refineries, and chemical operations. The pattern in most cases was the same: protestations of innocence, followed by court battles, followed eventually by submission to controls. During its operation, the APCD has prosecuted — count 'em — 42,000 criminal actions against polluters, and won over 90 percent of them.

Fuller, who snorts in disdain at attempts to set "human tolerance levels" of air pollution, takes the stand that "if it pollutes the air, it damn well shouldn't be released in the atmosphere. Period." Backed by tough laws, a fleet of radio-dispatched prowl cars, trained investigators, and a county-wide instant alert system that permit him to shut down industry at the push of a button on bad smog days, Fuller doesn't back up an inch — or need to.

APCD workers recall the day an industrial baron, whose name is known throughout the world (it's stamped on his product), stomped into Fuller's office, flanked by high-priced corporate attorneys. Pounding the desk, the industrialist thundered that he wasn't *about* to comply with an APCD directive to install smog abatement equipment at his factory. "Nobody," he snapped, "is going to tell *me* how to operate my company. You mess with me and I'll move my plant out of your damned county!"

"How soon," asked the unruffled Fuller, "can you leave?"

The man's attorneys called the following day to ask APCD to drop its planned suit. The smog equipment, they said, would be installed at once.

Such incidents are expected by pollution officials. They consider it a normal-enough reaction. Nobody likes to be tagged a polluter. Corporations detest being regulated — even when it's for their own benefit, as in the many instances when the installation of equipment or devices to trap pollutants has proved highly profitable.

One firm in Los Angeles County found after it began trapping pollutants that it was ending up with literally tons of odd "dust." The company's chemists ran a sample analysis and came up with a happy discovery. The funny "dust" assayed out at 30 percent nickel! They promptly pelletized the dust, shipped it out of state, and had the nickel extracted. In a short time, the pollution control equipment had been paid for several times over.

Pacific Smelting Company produces zinc oxide from
zinc scrap. The dust *it* trapped was found to contain zinc
oxide. They now reprocess the dust, reclaim the oxide, and
sell it.

Dust trapped in a baghouse unit by Morris P. Kirk Company, which makes prime lead ingots from the waste lead in
old batteries, was found to contain — you guessed it — prime
lead. The dust is now run through again, and Kirk makes
more lead ingots than it once did — and a better income.

When oil refineries were found to be losing gasoline
vapors while filling their tank trucks, they were required to
install equipment to trap the vapors before they could reach
the atmosphere. The refineries found, to their surprise, that
they had been losing a goodly amount of high-octane fuel
unnecessarily. Today the oil companies wouldn't consider
wasting all those nifty vapors — they are now saved and sold
to you at the corner gas station.

The list of savings effected in industry from the simple
good housekeeping practice of pollution control is virtually
endless. Even the fish-meal processors came up smelling like
roses. When canneries were told to lower the flame temperature in their ovens to reduce the amount of nitrogen oxides
being emitted, they found to their delight that they were
suddenly producing a more palatable product. Seems their
hot ovens had been scorching the fish!

If the tone of this discussion about the successes of the
air pollution control program in Los Angeles has given your
spirits a lift, forget it! The Los Angeles story is a minor
border skirmish in a ballooning global war. It is a partial victory
over some local industrial problems. Consider a larger one,

even in Los Angeles. The County sprawls over 4,083 square miles of territory, laced by freeways which intersect scores of communities growing in size like a Kansas prairie fire. Into this incredible basin are jammed nearly eight million people going their way in four million automobiles gulping eight million gallons of gasoline every day – a gallon per person per day.

To this gigantic Tomorrowland add a staggering array of business enterprises, each with its own peculiar pollution problems. In some cases we don't even know what the pollutants are, or how they mix with other pollutants from other sources in the atmosphere and sunlight, and we might not be able to cope with them even if we did know.

These are some of the problems facing Los Angeles and its neighboring counties. With some minor changes here and there, they are, or soon will be, the problems of most urban areas of the United States. Yet despite the warning flags flying from coast to coast, there are those who keep insisting it isn't all that dangerous, this smog. Neither is the gas chamber . . . until you breathe.

Run! Run! The Sky Is Falling!

It was a little more than two years ago that Frank Sinatra packed up his things, excoriated Los Angeles with a few well-modulated lines concerning smog, and decamped anon for Palm Springs, clear air, and a continuation of the Good Life.

It was not a gambit unparalleled. When the Middle Ages' road show version of air pollution, the Black Death, roamed the countryside, nobility, in a geste somewhat less than beau, retired to secluded country estates and left the plague to the peasants. It was recalled somewhat bitterly by the commoners that the plague was the first thing they had not been required to share with the royalty. To the consternation of the gentry, however, it came to pass that the Bubonic Plague was democratic as all get out. It forthwith diminished the chosen in droves, restructuring the caste system in the process.

Unfortunately for Frank, and a good many others who
have fled to safer ground, our own home-grown pox follows
almost apace. On the basis of reports last spring, Sinatra may
have to tell the good life good-bye — or seek it in Wyoming.
Palm Springs, playpen of the wealthy and paradise for the
afflicted, is the latest link in the smog chain being forged in
California.

Residents of the fabled desert city of sparkling days and
balmy, star-filled nights have reacted in typical fashion to the
smog infiltrating from Los Angeles by way of the mountain
passes. Some simply put their homes on the block and announced plans to move. Others called meetings, hired smog
experts, threatened to sue oil companies planning to build
refineries in nearby Banning and Beaumont. Older heads,
DP's from other smog areas, merely shake their heads sadly
as others seek to know if the pollution is a passing thing, or
permanent. Where smog has come it has never departed. It
stays, and grows.

Sadly, many of the citizens of Palm Springs are sufferers
of respiratory ailments. They came to the desert to escape
the blight which has now rejoined them. They hail from
affected areas throughout the nation: New York, Detroit,
Chicago, Cleveland, and other urbanized locales — including
Los Angeles, where ten thousand leave each year on their
doctors' orders. Most of them did not want to desert their
hometowns. It was a matter of life or death, literally.

Today, we know more about the effect of air pollution
on plants and animals than we do on humans. The reason is
simple: plants and animals can be isolated for testing over
long periods; humans cannot. Still, it is clear to most that air

pollution is a threat to human life and well-being. The American Medical Association's *Physician's Guide to Air Pollution* states: "Clearly, the lung, by virtue of its physiological function, is directly subject to infiltration and deposition by pollutants present in inhaled air." It notes that "evidence of life-long urban residence is dramatically apparent at autopsy in the form of lung pigmentation." The *Guide* adds, "The quality of respiratory health thus appears related to the quality of the air individuals are accustomed to breathing." Citing the air pollution disasters in London, England; Donora, Pennsylvania; and New York City, the AMA concludes these episodes have "demonstrated that air pollution can contribute significantly to excessive sickness and death rates."

If you've been skipping through this volume to find out whether it has a little sex to make it salable, you can stop at this spot. You may even want to underline this erotic paragraph for later reference. The hard fact of life is that smog may be lousing up our sexual capabilities. I use the word "may" because we aren't sure yet. So don't expect to start addressing your lover as "Dear Friend" for a while.

Still, the portent is clear. Studies on both mice and humans give strong indications that smog is a misogynic mist. Studies of female mice show they have fewer litters, fewer babies per litter, and a higher infant death rate. Dr. Otis Emik's experiments at the Statewide Air Pollution Research Center in Riverside, California spawned some distressing data on mice subjected to Los Angeles-type photochemical smog. The mice use more oxygen and work harder to do whatever mice do. In effect, they age faster and die sooner. The grim

PRETTY ORDINARY SMOGGY DAY IN L.A. It is predicted that most of this smog will be gone within ten years. This must be considered along with other estimates that disaster is due in five or six.

OPEN DUMP BURNS AT REDDING, CALIFORNIA

implications are that the same thing may be happening to humans. Dr. Emik made one other gloomy discovery: in smog, the male mice die sooner.

All this talk about mice that don't do overly well on smoggy days may not appear to be all that significant — unless, of course, you are a mouse. Forests that are dying from the oxidant in air pollution may seem similarly unimportant, except for the obvious economic and scenic loss. But there is another factor to consider: can pollutants that level giant trees and raise havoc with mice be harmless to humans? Or can it be we are in jeopardy? We can't be sure — yet. It may take years to show up, because the human life span is considerably longer than that of the mouse.

However, we do know enough to safely say that air pollution does have a marked effect on human activity, mental and physical. The ingredients in smog cause higher skin temperatures, reduce our ability to concentrate, act as a tranquilizer, increase our breathing rate, and make us either more quarrelsome or meek, depending on the type and concentration of pollutants in the air.

A six-year study of the performances of youngsters on the San Marino, California high school track team competing in long-distance races has shown that they run slower in smoggy weather. Those making the study could find no evidence that carbon monoxide, temperature, or humidity were related to the team's performance. The highest correlation to performance was the oxidant level the hour before each race. Runners frequently complained of chest pains, burning eyes, and general discomfort. Whether it was because of this discomfort or the possibility that oxidants are actually

DALLAS, TEXAS "SMAZE" — A rose by whatever name

CHICAGO SMOG. Being the "windy city" hasn't helped all that much.

making it difficult to breathe was not determined. The report of the study, "Oxidant Air Pollution and Athletic Performance," which appeared in the March 20, 1967 *Journal of the American Medical Association,* pointed out that the determination of precisely how oxidants in smog affect the performance of athletes is of "great importance" because "the relevance of these results to patients with borderline cardiac competence or chronic lung disease is completely different if the effect is directly on physiologic mechanisms such as ventilatory capacity rather than secondarily through an effect on motivation."

The San Marino study involved high school runners who are in peak physical condition and have the blessings of youth. It is quite another story for the elderly, and those suffering from respiratory ailments.

In an article printed in the Archives of Environmental Health in 1967, Dr. Harry Heimann points out the "growing evidence that morbidity and mortality from emphysema is increasing in the United States." Over a thirteen-year period from 1950 to 1963 the emphysema death rate zoomed from 8 to 80.2 per one million population. Medical experts are hard-pressed to find any reason other than air pollution to account for the sharp increase, which is especially apparent in urban areas.

That patients suffering from emphysema are adversely affected by smog is an established fact. Such patients, when placed in a clean air environment (on smoggy days) show marked improvement. Studies currently under way are seeking an answer to the obvious question: does air pollution *cause* the disease, as well as aggravate the condition of the

person already suffering from it? Most physicians would
probably be willing to bet that it does.

Dr. Roman L. Yanda, director of the Comprehensive
Pulmonary Care and Rehabilitation Program of Olive View
County Hospital in the San Fernando Valley, near Los Angeles, is literally commanding a fortress under siege most days
of the year. When smog dirties the air to a nuisance level for
most people, it becomes an all-out fight for survival for his
patients, some of whom hover between life and death in their
battle for breath.

In a lecture to the medical staff of Presbyterian Hospital
in Van Nuys, California, Yanda offered advice for physicians
and their patients — advice which, in some instances, sounds
strangely like that which might be laid down by Count Dra-
cula for neophyte vampires. Said Doctor Yanda, in discussing
what patients should do during smog attacks: "Go out early
in the a.m. or late p.m. Avoid crowds."

Yanda advises against use of hair sprays, cosmetics, or
kitchen aids; against smoking, alcohol, or fumes from irritating vapors such as ammonia, painting, or fumigation. In
planning ahead for smoggy days (emphysema sufferers must
do this), he advises extra sleep and postponed outdoor athletic activity.

His directions to patients often are oddly similar to
those issued by the Civil Defense authorites for an atomic
raid: "Dust-proof and allergy-proof the coolest room in the
house. Have adequate stocks of food and drink and recreational material on hand so trips to the store are not necessary
in smog. Telephone and radio should be available in or near
the room. The room should be set up so that a stay of several

ANALYSIS OF THERAPY OXYGEN TANKS SUBMITTED BY
THE HOSPITAL OF THE GOOD SAMARITAN HYPERBARIC UNIT

PERFORMED BY THE AIR POLLUTION CONTROL DISTRICT – COUNTY OF LOS ANGELES, TECHNICAL SERVICES DIVISION

COMPONENT:

	Parts Per Million by Volume:	
	Tank No. H.B.-1	Tank No. H.B.-2
SULFUR DIOXIDE	0.01	.01
FORMALDEHYDE	1.00	1.00
TOTAL WATER SOLUBLE ALDEHYDES (as HCHO)	1.00	1.00
OXIDES OF NITROGEN (as NO_2)	0.50	0.50
METHANE	23.00	26.00
ETHANE	0.35	0.35
PROPANE	0.17	0.16
ISOBUTANE	0.01	0.02
n-BUTANE	0.05	0.07
ISOPENTANE	0.01	0.02
2,2-Me_2-BUTANE	0.005	0.005
2-Me-PENTANE }		
2,3-Me_2-BUTANE	0.002	0.004
3-Me-PENTANE	0.003	0.003
n-HEXANE	0.003	0.004
CARBON MONOXIDE	4.00	5.00

THERE IS SOMETIMES A KIND OF BEAUTY
TO AIR POLLUTION. Also to caskets.
This is a power plant at night. It sometimes
looks nearly the same when it's not night.

days would not be uncomfortable."

For severe cases, Yanda's advice is simple. Leave Los
Angeles for some cleaner area. He admits few can afford to
do this, and even if they do, they probably would have to
return to the big city for the sophisticated medical-care facilities they require. As an alternative, he urges such patients to
keep track of coming smog alerts and "in advance, have
picked out another home, hotel, or motel . . . preferably air
conditioned . . . to which [they] can escape."

Dr. Yanda is not happy about the air quality *inside*
hospitals, either. "In the hospital, pollutants may range from
paint fumes and oil mists to cleaning and deodorant fumes,
insect sprays, and tobacco smoke.

"If a nurse were to give a patient a grossly contaminated
glass of water to drink after skillfully changing a sterile intra-
venous solution, she could expect loud criticism. In inhala-
tion therapy if we are responsible for the 'air' the patient
breathes some of the time, then ultimately we should become
responsible for the 'air' twenty-four hours a day whenever
medically indicated."

Constantly on the lookout for impurities in air which
his patients must breathe, Yanda suspected medical oxygen
might be a source of contaminants, and he investigated
breathing gases in Los Angeles. "I learned that they are extracted from local air, but I was assured it was 'filtered' prior
to being compressed."

Yanda had medical oxygen analyzed (five samples from
five different companies) and found levels of hydrocarbon up
to twenty-eight parts per million — fourteen times the level in
ordinary air! "U.S.P. (United States Pharmacopoeia) stan-

dards of gas quality were established in the 1930s, " Yanda explains, "when techniques for analyzing impurities in parts per million were in their infancy. Today, all gas suppliers routinely exceed these standards. And who gets that oxygen? The sickest of the people – the ones who need the cleanest air!"

Since there is no real control over the bulk of emissions which produce air pollution in Southern California, Dr. Yanda and other worried physicians have for some time been setting ground rules for patients with chest problems, including prohibition of cigarettes and a reduction of physical activity during smog sieges.

Finally, in 1969, the Los Angeles County Air Pollution Control District put into effect a system which warns school officials to cut back on physical activities when the ozone count in the atmosphere reaches .35 part per million (ppm) of air. When the .35 ppm figure is reached, which occurs about two weeks out of each month in the fall, a wide variety of athletic programs are affected, including football, track, and even water polo. Afternoon contests which are scheduled during periods of heavy smog are postponed or delayed until the smog dissipates below the .35 level.

Meantime, doctors have received news from studies being conducted at UCLA which will add to their problems. Tests conducted on rabbits indicate that a main ingredient of photochemical smog, nitrogen oxides, may interfere with the blood's ability to carry oxygen.

Nobody knows today to what extent we are injured by air pollution. Pollutants in the air range from lead, which is cumulative in the human body, to gases which can kill when

THESE ARE CARS IN LOS ANGELES. The cars are the principal cause of the smog hanging over them in this picture. This is ordinary traffic on the crowded freeways, although it looks like a funeral procession.

in high-enough concentration. Growing evidence indicates
that smog may well be a leading cause of chest ailments,
including bronchitis, emphysema, and lung cancer – all of
which have sharply increased and which are much more
prevalent in urban areas, where air pollution is heaviest.

A government publication on air pollution reports the
rate of lung cancer in large metropolitan centers of the
United States is *twice* that of rural areas – even after allow-
ances were made for smoking habits. In reporting on studies
conducted with mice, the publication notes: "Mice which
had been sensitized with influenza virus and then exposed to
ozonized gasoline (simulated photochemical smog) developed
bronchogenic cancer of the type humans develop. In another
study, hamsters exposed repeatedly to intratracheal adminis-
trations of a particulate form of hydrocarbon that is found
much more frequently in city air than in rural air all developed bronchogenic cancer."

Of course all these reports, studies, tests, and the like
concerning the *effect* of air pollution are necessary because
we are not able to bring the *cause* (the polluters) under control. The polluters frequently deny they are polluters and,
barring that fiction, deny that air pollution is as serious as is
claimed in most reports.

Charles Heinan, Chief Engineer in Emission Control and
Chemical Development for Chrysler Corporation, seemed optimistic about the health aspects of smog when he addressed
the National Pollution Control Exposition and Conference
in Texas in the spring of 1968. "There is a good possibility,"
said Heinan, "that considerable nonsense is being preached
about potential health effects because there are many contra-

ANALYSIS OF GASES FROM VARIOUS MEDICAL GAS SUPPLIERS

Performed by the University of California Air Pollution Monitoring Station, Riverside.

COMPRESSED AIR SOURCE:

CONSTITUENT PRESENT:

	Company A₁	Company A₂	Company B.	Company C.	Company D.
METHANE — P.P.M.	1.35	2.00	1.36	1.57	
ETHANE — P.P.M.	0.01	0.02	0.01	0.03	
ETHYLENE — P.P.M.	0.01	—	0.01	0.08	
PROPANE — P.P.M.	0.01	0.01	0.01	0.02	
PROPYLENE — P.P.M.	—	—	—	TR	
ACETYLENE — P.P.M.	TR	—	0.01	—	
BUTANE — P.P.M.	—	TR	—	0.01	

COMPRESSED OXYGEN SOURCE:

CONSTITUENT PRESENT:

	Company A₁	Company A₂	Company B.	Company C.	Company D.
METHANE — P.P.M.	26.60	27.70	14.20	16.00	
ETHANE — P.P.M.	0.40	0.50	0.06	0.22	
ETHYLENE — P.P.M.	0.04	0.11	—	0.01	
PROPANE — P.P.M.	0.09	0.10	0.19	0.08	
PROPYLENE — P.P.M.	—	—	—	—	
ACETYLENE — P.P.M.	—	—	—	—	
BUTANE — P.P.M.	—	TR	—	0.07	

METHANE BACKGROUND SIGNAL (AMBIENT) — 1.2 PPM.

dictions; but by the same token, there is no certainty about what portion of it is important." Referring to photochemical smog in Los Angeles as a "nuisance which should not be tolerated," Heinan admitted it affects vegetation and "may have other economic effects." He then cleared that hurdle for the automobile, which supplies 85 percent of the smog in Southern California, by adding: "Fortunately, it does not appear to have the major long-range health effects which have been long suspected. Massive surveys reported by Hammond and Buell definitely show that there is no relation between the incidence of photochemical smog and lung cancer and certainly raise some serious questions about its relation to other lung diseases. This is good news indeed."

Somebody forgot to tell zoology professor Kenneth Watt of the University of California, who in August 1969 predicted mass deaths from air pollution in the Los Angeles basin within six years. Professor Watt said: "It is now clear that air pollution concentrations are rising in California at a rate such that mass mortality incidents can be expected in specific areas, such as Long Beach, by the 1975-76 winter. The proportion of the population which will die in these incidents will first equal, then exceed, that for the 1952 London smog disaster."

I don't for a moment doubt the professor, but I have unbounded faith that the auto manufacturers will meet the challenge in any such event — with a longer, lower, sleeker, more powerful line of hearses.

More Like
A Mortician

Early in the 1950s, baffled research foresters watched
helplessly as a phantom plant disease began to stalk relent-
lessly through the towering San Bernardino and San Gabriel
mountains, above the Los Angeles-Riverside basin. Two
things concerned the forestry officials. The mountains held
some of the finest and most important stands of timber in all
of California; and, so far, nobody had the faintest clue as to
the nature of the mystery sickness. They called it simply: X
Disease.

Hardest hit were the tall and stately old Ponderosa
Pines, the southernmost range of these great trees in California. They had stood unconquered against the fiercest
blows of nature since before America was a nation. Now they
sickened and died within five years. Their gaunt brown skele-
tons were beginning to pepper the green mountainsides.

X Disease was simple to recognize. The symptoms were

unmistakable and followed a pattern that was to become
terribly familiar. The needles developed an odd yellow
mottle, and instead of retaining four or five years growth,
there was only the current season's. After awhile, the
branches took on a tufted appearance, the needles pointing
heavenward. Finally, the fibrous root system would deteriorate, heralding the coming of death.

By any yardstick, the demise of the Ponderosa – and
other trees and shrubs in the mountains – was a disaster.
Ecology, economy, and recreation depended upon the trees,
which provide a stablized watershed, wood products, and a
playground area that in 1968 was to draw almost nine million
visitors.

The San Bernardino range divides the vast and rapidly
growing coastal lands from the awesome Mojave Desert and is
a natural attraction to the millions who populate the area
from San Diego to Los Angeles. An area of heavy snows in
the winter and cool forests in the summer, the mountains
provide every type of recreation imaginable, from skiing to
hiking – and all within a two-hour freeway trip from Los
Angeles and the nearby San Fernando Valley.

Because the trees were so important, research and field
work was stepped up in an attempt to isolate the cause of X
Disease and halt its savage inroads. The first break came in
1962. A scientific paper published by *Plant Disease Reporter*
outlined the findings of two plant pathologists and an Arrowhead district ranger, who had concluded a study of the dying
trees. No ordinary disease or insect was involved! Said the
investigators, there was no evidence of "the consistent presence of pathogenic organisms." They advanced instead, the

THIS IS A PONDEROSA PINE at fashionable Lake Arrowhead, California. Over two-thirds of the Ponderosa are dead — from air pollution. Once damaged by smog, the trees always die . . . usually within 10 years. People take longer.

idea that the villain in this instance might be "drought, air pollution or a combination of the two."

Other scientists picked up the scent. It was already known that smog had been damaging plants for a decade in the San Bernardino Valley. Could it be that the polluted air was beginning to invade the higher elevations in amounts sufficient to kill trees? A program was initiated to find out.

Needles of the Ponderosa pine were subjected to air with ozone, while other Ponderosa needles were given filtered air. Within a few days at .5 parts per million (ppm), the familiar mottle of X Disease appeared. The filtered air needles showed no mottle.

Later work substantiated the findings and laid the blame squarely on air pollution. In 1967, the research which had been conducted under the auspices of the Pacific Southwest Forest and Range Experiment Station was transferred to the University of California at Riverside, the Statewide Air Pollution Research Center, with Dr. Paul Miller, a plant pathologist, in charge. Dr. Miller and his associates have concentrated their efforts on measuring the susceptibility of various species of trees to smog, identifying damage, studying other variables such as soil, moistures, etc., and even testing to try to find varieties of pine that can resist smog.

To date, not a single remedy has been found which can halt or even impede the gray-brown plague that moves up through the pines almost daily during the summer months. It comes at will, and it kills with impunity.

Today, approximately two-thirds of the Ponderosa Pines are either dead or soon will be. Doctor Miller, who spends most of his time on the mountain near Lake Arrowhead studying the growing carnage, talks with the bitterness of a man who has been asked to stop a cavalry charge with a hatpin. Chatting quietly over a soft drink at Lake Arrowhead Village last summer, he admitted we have little chance of saving *any* of the Ponderosa. "Once one of those trees is hit by ozone," he said, "it's going to die. It is only a function of time. There is no way — nothing we can do. We have tried everything we can think of. You'd have to enclose them all in a carbon-filtered greenhouse to have a chance." He pointed to dead and dying trees which blotched the hill across the Lake. "Once they suffer damage — even a little — it's a hundred percent fatal. All we can do is walk around and count the dead ones. I feel more like a plant mortician than a plant pathologist. When we stop the smog, we'll stop the dying. That's it."

Putting a dollar price tag on the trees is impractical. They are worth much more than the price a lumberman might pay. One must compute the price in terms of the loss of beauty to the area, which loss in turn directly affects every business connected with recreation. When the beauty goes, so will the visitors. The trees help the mountains retain the moisture that comes with the rains and snow. With the loss of a tree, there is an accompanying loss of water, which can then pour over the denuded earth with the inevitable erosion and threat of flood.

Those who own or are planning to purchase a lot in the mountains face the possibility of losing the trees on that lot. They will bear the financial and aesthetic loss. Insurance companies will not write a policy to cover owners for trees lost to air pollution.

A psychologist would have the time of his life in a study of the public's reaction to air pollution. All the worst elements of man's nature seem to surface. Most communities would rather not talk about smog. When we tried to interview business owners and residents of Lake Arrowhead for a documentary film to be seen on KNBC in Los Angeles, nobody wanted to talk. We ran across people who were evasive, frightened, and belligerent. Most seemed embarrassed. They talked furtively of smog, as though it were a social disease. They appeared to feel exactly as I did as a little boy when my classmates discovered I had the itch. One lady, a member of a local homeowners' association, admitted she knew of the smog problem, but said the group had never discussed the matter at its meetings. A Chamber of Commerce official said he knew there was a small amount of smog damage, but "the forest rangers are taking care of it." None of them wanted to appear on TV, but suggested that "maybe Joe, down the street. . . ." Joe wouldn't talk, either.

Downright anger we got from the sales representative of Arrowhead Development Company, a subsidiary of Boise Cascade Company, which bought Lake Arrowhead and is now busily developing the property and selling lots. This chap was congenial enough at the outset, but exploded at the mention of dying trees and smog. He let me know in explicit terms that his company is "selling clean and green" and that there is no smog and no trees dying from it. He added, as emphasis, that any such talk could get me – and NBC – sued "for every damn penny you've got." I felt very flattered to be included in such august company, and later impressed my colleagues with the threat. I did not tell my bank, although they would have found much humor in it. At any rate, this fellow did not wish to be interviewed, either, because "our main office in Chicago says we shouldn't comment on smog."

"Not even 'no comment'?"

"No."

The latest sales flyers from Lake Arrowhead Development Company still are undaunted. They promote "clear mountain air . . . pine forests." To our certain knowledge, however, the air is still smoggy, the trees are still dying, and the scientists are still counting.

Smog data for the mountain regions released by Dr. Miller in 1969 are highly revealing, and are recommended reading for those who doubt the grim facts related here. Shown in the chart below are the average daily maximum figures for total oxidant in the air in parts per hundred million, from May through October 1968. The figures appearing below the oxidant numbers are the number of days that the state standard of 15.0 pphm was exceeded. The state standard is that beyond which damage occurs to plants and materials; i.e., trees, shrubs, rubber tires, etc. On several days, the oxidant level in the Arrowhead district far exceeded the standard, nearly reaching the alert stage. The chart compares the Arrowhead area with Riverside, which is situated 5,000 feet below.

ARROWHEAD AREA	MAY	JUNE	JULY	AUG.	SEPT.	OCT.
Total Oxidant	20.4	23	20.8	19.4	22	15
Days Standard Exceeded	9.	23	24	23	15	8
RIVERSIDE AREA						
Total Oxidant	18.4	13	20.6	19	26	24

Source: Statewide Air Pollution Research Center

The decimation of plants and trees by air pollution is not a new problem. However, man's *giving a damn* whether the trees die or not is a fairly new and pleasant phenomenon. In the America of a century or so ago, there were vast virgin forests. Trees were something chopped down to build a cabin or cleared away to plant crops. They were useful for Indians to hide behind until a settler got within barbering range. When industry came along, our forests had an enemy far more terrible than the occasional frontiersman. Belching stacks, smelters, and chemical operations could demolish the landscape without lifting an axe. Examples are plentiful. One government publication tells of a smelter in British Columbia that destroyed plant life fifty miles away with its monthly

SOME AREAS OF TENNESSEE HAVE TREES. This one doesn't. Instead, it has a copper-mining/smelting operation. Trees are green. Copper is the color of pennies.

output of 18,000 tons of sulfur pollution. In 1910, a smelter in Montana raped the countryside of vegetation in a ten-mile radius. The devastation in the vicinity of these smelter operations is so complete it gives the appearance of having undergone an artillery barrage.

There is no means by which we can accurately assess the cost, ecologically or aesthetically, for the wounds we are inflicting on nature through air pollution. However, we can place our dollar losses with fair success. Man has always been good at that.

The financial beating we are suffering from plant and crop losses due to smog is truly staggering. The horrendous damage and the resultant costs were summed up in 1968 by Dr. Seymour Calvert, director of the Statewide Air Pollution Center in Riverside, California. According to Dr. Calvert, citrus growers in the Los Angeles Basin are losing almost $33 million annually. Tests have shown that citrus trees in smoggy air lose 30 percent more leaves and often produce only half as much mature fruit as they would if raised in clean air. Dr. Calvert estimates the California loss of ornamental plants (homeowners and businesses) at perhaps $192 million each year.

In discussing the growing losses to pollution, Dr. Calvert warned of enormous potential damage in the rich San Joaquin and Salinas Valleys. "It should be pointed out," said Dr. Calvert, "that no significant plant damage has yet been found in the Salinas Valley. However, an episode occurred on July 25, 1967, which indicates that pollution in the valley is increasing and that serious injury can be expected in the not-too-distant future."

Even Christmas-tree growers in Southern California are taking heavy losses. Approximately one-third of the trees are damaged, with perhaps 10 percent unmarketable. Trees which are not so badly injured can be painted or sprayed with fake snow.

tained in California: almost a quarter of a billion dollars, with the amount rising yearly. Anticipated losses for the San Joaquin and Salinas Valleys bring the grand total to $411 million annually.

In computing the effect of air pollution on land values, Dr. Calvert used Lake Arrowhead as an example. Land there, he pointed out, is worth from $50,000 to $60,000 per acre . . . with the price going up $5,000 to $7,000 higher for forested land. He added that "there are at least 20,000 acres severely affected by ozone in this area, which represents an estimated land value contributed by trees of $120 million."

The figures are there, but they make little sense to the common man. Eleven billion dollars, give or take a few million, lost to smog in Southern California in the last two decades. That much is chalked up to air pollution *yearly* for the nation. Only the eye of a Swiss banker is suited to digesting such sums. Losing billions, we spend millions to fight air pollution. We attack it with the sagacity of a man entering The Four Seasons with a buck and a half. Onassis would spend more at a clam digging than we allot for research.

In the overall picture, unfortunately, the money we've lost and the money we will spend — however much — may be of little consequence. At this late hour, we shall be sorely pressed to salvage our environment, no matter how high we stack the blue chips. The signs, some of them rather obscure at the moment, are everywhere — but too often on the back page. If you check closely, you will find them.

The English, too, are in trouble; their ancient oak trees are surrendering to urbanization in general and air pollution in particular. The British are attacking the problem in time-honored scientific tradition: from the back door. They are trying to plant trees that are more resistant to pollution. It is simpler, in the short-range scheme of things, than bucking the polluters.

A recent study shows that grapes are the latest victim of smog. The foul air reduces their sugar content, yellows their leaves, withers the vines. The public, predictably, will simply adapt to sour grapes from ratty little vines, and Robin Hood

ESTIMATED ANNUAL COST OF PLANT DAMAGE BY PHOTOCHEMICAL SMOG
(California)

Present

Vegetables		$ 10,000,000
Citrus (Southern California)		32,500,000
Flowers		2,000,000
Ornamentals (Los Angeles only)		144,000,000
Ornamentals (remainder of California)		48,000,000
Trees (Lake Arrowhead region)		12,000,000
	Subtotal	$ 248,500,000

Anticipated

Grapes, cotton, alfalfa, tomatoes (San Joaquin)		$ 60,000,000
Citrus (San Joaquin)		96,000,000
Lettuce, celery, tomatoes (Salinas)		7,000,000
	Subtotal	$ 163,000,000
	GRAND TOTAL	$ 411,500,000

AIR POLLUTION IN SOUTHERN CALIFORNIA affects almost everything, including grapes . . . stunting their growth, draining the leaves of color, and reducing sugar content. On the left is a smoggy bunch. On the right are grapes grown in clean air. Some people deny smog can harm things. Sour grapes.

films will be made with painted backdrops.

There are ample precedents to indicate the above. We adapt and adjust, just as East Germans have finally become "contented prisoners." We observe the deepening shadows with a puzzled acquiesence. After all, we live in an advanced society fairly smothered in chromium conveniences. It is reminiscent of the fellow speeding down a country road in his car. When a worried passenger inquired, "Do you know where we're going?" the answer came back: "No, but we're making damned good time!"

Those who have stopped long enough to check the ecological road map *know* where we're going, but they are not heeded. When one of us lifts his voice in protest that we are murdering the only things we have worth keeping, he is promptly written off as "one of those nutty bird-watchers or nature-lovers" who obviously doesn't understand the really critical issues of the day, such as maintaining the 27.5 percent oil depletion allowance.

Even when men of impeccable credentials hoist the warning pennants, they are shunted off to the backwaters of the news pages, in favor of a love triangle. Such was the case, recently, when Professor E.F. Watt of the University of California appeared before a House subcommittee probing into social ills in our country. Professor Watt said that trees are going to be "largely a memory in the United States in 2000 A.D." He warned that the U.S. may run out of farmland and forests unless population and urbanization are controlled. Unless substitutes are discovered, he said, we will have only 84 percent of the land needed to feed our people (expected to number 331 million) by the end of this century. He added

MIDNIGHT SMOKE IN LOUISVILLE — Not appreciably different from Noon Smoke in Louisville

that the first lands converted to farming will be recreation
areas.

The professor also pointed to a peril from smog: it
could bring on an ice age by screening off the sun's warmth.
If that theory doesn't interest you, then flip the coin. A rise
in the earth's temperature caused by the heat of the sun
being trapped by a smog layer could create a global "greenhouse." This would eventually melt the polar icecaps, raising
the level of the oceans, inundating the major seaports of the
world – and making some brand new ocean-front property
available in Santa Fe, New Mexico.

Age of Consent

Government and industry, in the jargon of business are "in bed together." And the coupling is not all that unnatural. Industry has immense power and wealth; government is fraught with fellows who have no aversion to either. Of Washington's curious mix — industry men who are government appointees, former government figures now in the employ of industry, lobbyists who happily service both — most are working for special interests. The only large group not adequately represented is the American public.

Now in light of this well-known situation, it is not surprising that big industrial and business powers are able to blunt or thwart any threat to their corporate happiness. Any problem, big or little, can be handled. Anyone who doubts this has only to study the recent case of the federal suit against the Big Four auto manufacturers, charging violation of Section I of the Sherman Act. The complaint, Civil No.

69-75-JWC, filed January 10, 1969, in the waning days of the
Johnson Administration, was a civil suit, although it was no
"state secret" that the Federal Grand Jury investigation
which preceded the suit turned up information that many
felt could have supported a criminal indictment.

In the fall of 1969, after the Nixon Administration
moved into power in Washington, the Justice Department
"elected" to settle the suit, which charged a conspiracy to
delay development of smog devices for cars, out of court, via
a consent decree. The decree, if approved by a federal court,
would let the auto makers off without so much as a delay of
the game penalty. In the type of logic peculiar to the envi-
rons of Washington, D.C., the Big Four would be permitted
to walk away without admitting guilt — while at the same
time promising not to do such naughty things again. The
settlement would do one more thing which is very important
to the Detroit industrialists; it would lock the Grand Jury
testimony and other thousands of documents away from
public gaze, sweeping any damaging or incriminating evidence
under the carpet.

When the Justice Department announced its plans, the
Executive Branch remained aloof and an enraged bellow
arose from millions of Americans, especially those forced to
exist in smog-ridden cities. They sensed that Washington was
dealing "seconds" to John Q. in this little game of blackjack.
The decision to let the car manufacturers off cheap marked
one of the most brazen displays of corporate power — and
governmental weakness — in history.

What were the charges that the Justice Department so
casually dismissed? They are printed below, and the reader is

"That's a great anti-suit device! . . . How effective is it against smog?"

urged to read them and make his own determination as to how the case should have been handled.

VI

OFFENSE ALLEGED

12. Beginning at least as early as 1953, and continuing thereafter up to and including the date of this complaint, the defendants and co-conspirators have been engaged in a combination and conspiracy in unreasonable restraint of the aforesaid interstate trade and commerce in motor vehicle air pollution control equipment in violation of Section 1 of the Sherman Act (15 U.S.C. §1).

13. The aforesaid combination and conspiracy has consisted of a continuing agreement, understanding, and concert of action among the defendants and co-conspirators, the substantial terms of which have been and are:

    (a)   to eliminate all competition among themselves in the research, development, manufacture and installation of motor vehicle air pollution control equipment; and

    (b)   to eliminate competition in the purchase of patents and patent rights from other parties covering motor vehicle air pollution control equipment.

14. For the purpose of forming and effectuating the aforesaid combination and conspiracy, the defendants and

co-conspirators did those things which they combined and conspired to do, including, among other things, the following:

(a) agreed that all industry efforts directed at the research, development, manufacture and installation of motor vehicle air pollution control equipment should be undertaken on a non-competitive basis;

(b) agreed to seek joint appraisal of patents and patent rights submitted to any of them by persons not parties to a cross-licensing agreement entered into on July 1, 1955, and amended and renewed periodically, and to require "most-favored-purchaser" treatment of all parties to the cross-licensing agreement if any one were licensed by a person not a party to that agreement;

(c) agreed to install motor vehicle air pollution control equipment only upon a uniform date determined by agreement, and subsequently agreed on at least three separate occasions to attempt to delay the installation of motor vehicle air pollution control equipment:

(1) in 1961 the defendants agreed among themselves to delay installation of "positive crankcase ventilation" on vehicles for sale outside of California until the model year 1963, despite the fact that this antipollution device could have been installed nationally for the model year 1962 and that at least some automobile manufacturers

expressed willingness to do so, in the absence of a contrary industry-wide agreement;

(2)   in late 1962 and extending into 1963, the defendants agreed among themselves to delay installation of an improvement to the positive crankcase ventilation device, an improvement which the California Motor Vehicle pollution Control Board had indicated it would make mandatory;

(3)   in early 1964 the defendants agreed among themselves to attempt to delay the introduction of new exhaust pollution control measures on motor vehicles sold in California until the model year 1967; despite the fact that all were capable of installing the improvement for the model year 1966, the defendants agreed to tell California regulatory officials that installation of exhaust antipollution measures would be technologically impossible before 1967, and only under regulatory pressure made possible by competing device manufacturers not in the automobile industry did the defendants agree to a California regulatory requirement that exhaust devices be installed for the model year 1966; and

(d)   agreed to restrict publicity relating to research and development efforts and development efforts concerning the motor vehicle air pollution problem.

VII

EFFECTS
_____

15.   The aforesaid combination and conspiracy has had, among others, the following effects:

   (a)   hindering and delaying the research, development, and manufacture — both by the defendants and co-conspirators and by others not parties to the agreements alleged herein — and the installation of motor vehicle air pollution control equipment;

   (b)   restricting and suppressing competition among the defendants and co-conspirators in the research, development, manufacture and installation of motor vehicle air pollution control equipment; and

   (c)   restricting and suppressing competition in the purchase of patents and patent rights covering motor vehicle air pollution control equipment.

The Justice Department's move to settle the complaint without a trial spawned an immediate rash of other suits seeking to intervene and to open the Grand Jury testimony for public review. Los Angeles filed a $100 million damage suit; Chicago followed with a $3 billion suit for damages filed by attorney James Torshen for two Chicago Aldermen. The State of California announced it might sue (and later did), and forty-six Congressmen petitioned the federal court to reject the proposed settlement.

Consumer advocate Ralph Nader flayed the Justice

Department for the proposed settlement, calling the consent decree a "basic fraud" and "not worth the paper it's written on." Nader said it would be impossible for the government to enforce the agreement since there are but six lawyers in the Antitrust Division of the Justice Department and hundreds of such complicated settlements.

When the showdown in what was being called the "antitrust suit of the century" finally arrived late in October, it was predicably cut and dried. Judge Jesse W. Curtis presided at a hearing in the U.S. District Court in Los Angeles. Into the jammed room came the Big Four attorneys, a glittering array of the best legal talent in the country. They might have stayed home and sent a runner; Judge Curtis could have called in the verdict. The decree was promptly approved. The auto makers were home free.

Judge Curtis did issue an order impounding the transcripts and all exhibits. He said the material would be made available to all who need access to it in the course of filing suits against the auto manufacturing concerns. Already in the hands of the State of California lawyers are approximately two hundred thousand documents from the federal investigation.

While the politicians carried the day for the carriage trade in this antitrust action, it may have been a costly victory. The public is emotionally involved right up to its smog-filled eyeballs, especially in the large urban centers. These citizens may not be forgiving of high public officials who appear weak-kneed in dealing with polluters.

One of the more laughable utterances of the entire

episode was that of Assistant Attorney General Richard W. McLaren, chief of the Justice Department's Antitrust Division. He called for approval of the consent decree as a move which would permit the Department to continue its "strong antitrust enforcement program." One wonders by what process of rationalization the granting of this decree can be construed as "strong" enforcement?

Political realists never gave the suit against the auto manufacturers much chance of getting to court. The hard facts are that when big business and the public interest butt heads, big business will usually prevail. Industry, after all, has money, superb legal talent, and friends in high places. The people are generally short on all three counts.

One man unlikely to give up in the battle to run Detroit up a tree is Los Angeles County Supervisor Kenneth Hahn, who, lance in hand, went to the lists with the auto makers in 1953. He has been nipping and worrying at them like a rat terrier after a moose herd ever since. Instrumental in bringing about the Grand Jury investigation, he later pushed for the Los Angeles intervention in the consent decree.

A Hahn letter to Henry Ford II in 1953 brought an answer that still bedevils the auto makers, for it painted a portrait of an industry either ignorant of the air pollution menace or one that didn't give a damn — or both. Hahn's letter was answered not by Henry, but by a hapless publicity man, who got more blame and attention than he deserved. Hahn had questioned Ford about smog and the automobile's role, and had queried the company about possible devices to effect a cure. Ford's answer:

MR. KENNETH HAHN
Los Angeles County Supervisor
Los Angeles, Cal.

Dear Mr. Hahn:

The Ford engineering staff, although mindful
that automobile engines produce exhaust
gases, feels these waste vapors are dissipated
in the atmosphere quickly and do not present
an air pollution problem. Therefore, our
research department has not conducted any
experimental work aimed at totally eliminating these gases.

The fine automotive powerplants which
modern-day engineers design do not "smoke."
Only aging engines subjected to improper care
and maintenance burn oil.

To date, the need for a device which will
more effectively reduce exhaust vapors has
not been established. However, considerable
research has been directed toward more efficient fuel combustion.

Yours very truly,

DAN J. CHABEK
News Department

Since that memorable "Go way, boy, you bother me"
letter, the automobile manufacturers maintain they have

expended millions of dollars and mountains of man-hours in
the search for devices to curb pollution from their product.
The public is largely unsympathetic to this plea. It also exhibits faint interest in the atmospheric carrot perennially
advanced by Detroit in the form of the "ten-year plan," at
the end of which smog will surely have dissipated. This is
understandable, when scientists of some note are offering up
timetables of their own showing smog disasters with accompanying deaths as early as 1976. A cynic might suspect a
nefarious scheme whereby Detroit will simply outlast its
pesterers by four years.

What is the "real" story behind the Big Four's failure to
come up with devices which can reduce or eliminate automotive pollutants? There are any number of theories making the
rounds. We have selected four of the more interesting for
listing here. Take your pick.

1.   Detroit already has a device which will reduce the smog
to the level desired in California (whose standards are more
strict than the rest of the nation) but doesn't want to put it
on until the rest of the country has the same standards. Until
then such equipment would be optional outside California
. . . and such options might not be as attractive as windshield
aerials and other goodies, and therefore not salable.

2.   Essentially the same as No. 1, but this theory holds that
Detroit *could* have the device, but doesn't want to spend the
money to develop it until it is required, nationally.

3.   Detroit has no interest in developing devices to eliminate

pollutants from the internal combustion engine, when it is planning a switch in a few years to gas turbines or steam engine-driven vehicles.

4. Detroit simply hasn't the know-how to cope with the complex thermochemical problems being encountered. This theory lacks the intrigue of the other possibilities listed, but probably comes closer to the truth — perhaps in conjunction with the motives of No. 2: the desire to make a buck on the deal, no matter how it works out.

If in fact Detroit is in over its scientific head in the battle to put the clamps on automotive emissions, it is not alone. The answers have eluded the nation's best scientific talent. The toughest nut to crack is nitrogen oxide (NO_x), which is formed whenever air is super-heated — as in the combustion chamber of the internal combustion engine. Once formed, NO_x does not readily "break down" to nitrogen and carbon dioxide — harmless ingredients. Instead, it leaves the exhaust and enters the atmosphere, where it "cooks" in the sunlight to become nitrogen dioxide — four times more toxic. This then becomes a major constituent of photochemical smog, the rusty brown veil which has become a landmark over Los Angeles, wreaking immense havoc with plants, materials, and people.

The solution to automotive smog must be found — and quickly — if man and his environment are to avoid catastrophic consequences. Our alternative is clear, and is one with fighter pilots of World War II, who phrased it thusly: "Get — or get got."

CARS MAKE ALL KINDS OF SMOG. Here, some are burning at Alexandria, Virginia. In the background is George Washington Masonic National Monument. The cars are also monumental. The picture was taken in 1966.

The Taco Hypothesis

The mule, old-timers claim, had one great advantage over
the automobile. When a mule refused to perform in an
acceptable manner, one could induce a return to duty and
civility by requisitioning a medium-size peeled branch and
beating the hell out of him. Such direct and comforting
recourse has been denied man in bouts with his car. Vigor-
ously applied blows directed at the family auto are more
therapeutic for owner than for vehicle. Thus, the car, frequently more obstinate than the mule, seems to defy builder
and buyer alike. It is doing so with considerable success in
the matter of exhaust pollutants, balking at it does at standards established to render it fumeless.

Over the past decades, some gains have been made
through the edict and money-wrench route, to be sure, but at
a price which makes it a dubious victory. Hydrocarbons have
been reduced, to some extent, but devices designed and

installed for that purpose by Detroit's car makers have sharply increased the emission of nitrogen oxides in the process. The oxides of nitrogen (NO_x), unfortunately, are more dangerous than the hydrocarbons. Attempts by the auto manufacturers to reduce the NO_x have been notably unsuccessful.

The problem lies in the modern internal combustion engine, a thing of high compression and temperature. The toxic NO_x is formed from air (mostly nitrogen and oxygen) under heat and pressure, and the higher the heat the more NO_x. Ergo, the more efficient the engine, the more it pollutes. The solution? Reduce heat and pressure. Sure, that cuts the amount of NO_x. It also lowers the engine efficiency and horsepower, and we head back toward the Model A.

This perplexing situation has caused a good deal of mumbling and shuffling of the feet in Detroit, with periodic announcement of the aforementioned "ten-year" plans. Other phrases, such as "systems approach," are popular, but seem chiefly useful to justify the need for ten more years. Meanwhile, in the Los Angeles Basin, trees die, people sicken, and bicycle tires rot in five months . . . from automotive smog.

It was one of these ten-year pronouncements that led to development of the film documentary, "The Slow Guillotine." In the process of researching the film, I decided Detroit just might be in over its head, scientifically. The problem was obviously a thermochemical one, which the manufacturers seemed to be attacking in a mechanical manner.

I decided to call on an old friend and colleague who might be able to lick the problem: Milton Farber. Farber is a thermodynamicist, a specialist in that field of science that grapples with the mysteries of heat, its action and reaction. He is one of the world's foremost minds in the business of thermochemistry. He may even be *the* best. In August 1969, he presented the keynote lecture at his session of the First International Conference on Thermodynamics and Calorimetry in Warsaw, Poland. His address was received enthusiastically by attendees from twenty-six nations, including the Russians, who hold Farber in high esteem.

World Who's Who in Science lists Farber as having "Developed new method for determination of thermodynamic studies; pioneered research in electrical propulsion in the United States; originated use of heavy particles for electric propulsion; and ion synthesis of chemical compounds."

BORN IN A TACO SHOP, the double-chamber catalyst muffler shown here may be the long-sought answer to automotive pollution.

Farber earned his reputation early. Working with Professor Willard Libby at the University of California at Berkeley in the months just prior to World War II, young Farber was one of a handful of men in the United States probing the mysteries of the atom. His paper on the separation of uranium isotopes, published as a graduate student, was one of the last made public on the subject prior to a clampdown on all information about atomic research.

During the war, Farber was assigned as pilot plant supervisor in charge of design and method of improvement of the diffusion process for Manhattan District Project, the program which developed the first atom bomb. Showing his typical forthright ingenuity on the project, he overcame a severe shortage of Ph.D. scientists by hiring untrained mountain girls as operators for the hundreds of cyclatrons used in the uranium separation process. The girls, many of whom could not read or write — and who got their first pair of real shoes as part of their job — promptly became known as "Farber's Hillbillies." Says Farber: "They made great cyclatron operators!"

Following the war, Farber spent ten years as a senior scientist at the California Institute of Technology's Jet Propulsion Laboratory in Pasadena, California. He later held executive positions with Aerojet-General Corporation, Hughes Tool Company, and Rocket Power, Inc., a solid propellant company in Mesa, Arizona.

It was at Rocket Power that I first met Farber, who was in charge of the company's Pasadena research laboratories. I was staff assistant to RPI's President, Charles Bartley, the man who'd invented America's first modern solid propellant.

Among my duties was responsibility for releasing information on company projects to the public.

Farber's operation always made interesting copy for the newspapers, although the secrecy of his projects and their jaw-breaking, mind-bending subject matter made translation for public consumption a tough assignment. He dealt with far-out research that could guide development of higher-energy rocket fuels, for example. I recall endless hours of labor, trying to popularize "The Heat of Formation and Entropy of Boron Oxyfluoride" so that it could be under-stood and appreciated by housewives. When I bogged down, I could depend on Farber to help humanize the equations. He has that rare knack that escapes most research scientists: the ability to communicate with the layman.

I remember one program the laboratory was working on: "A Mathematical Model for the Containment of a Spheri-cal Plasma." Isn't that a dandy? Farber finally rescued me by explaining," We're trying to make some round-shaped ball lightning; the stuff that used to float around and sometimes kill grandma's cow." Right away we had a story that was carried in newspapers all over the world. Of course, the scien-tific reason for the investigation of ball lightning was that nobody had ever been able to make it. If they could, it might hold the key to control of hydrogen power for peaceful purposes.

Farber and I became close friends. I marveled at the way he always seemed to come up with the answer, even on the "hairiest" scientific projects. More than once a Farber answer replaced a previous Russian answer that he had proved wrong. Apparently they remembered, the Russians, because they were careful to have Farber in Warsaw for the international conference. When he arrived, the Soviet scientists told him they had been watching his work for many years with keen interest. No doubt.

Blunt, outspoken, unforgiving of any colleague who does not measure up to *his* exacting demands, Farber has been known to fire two Ph.D chemists off the same job in as many days. In addition, he has some of the quirks associated with most scientists. I never did try to understand them; I just accepted them. For instance, he has never been known to eat a *whole* piece of pie. He will split the piece, if he can find someone to share it. Otherwise, he waves the dessert away. Unlike many scientists, Farber is highly sociable, loves a joke, and once whipped off a heat formula for *girls* at the request of a ribbing reporter. "That's a basic heat formula," said Farber, with a straight face. "There's a hell of a lot of entropy going on there."

So it was natural that I should call on Farber one afternoon late in 1967. I told him I would buy him a taco and half a piece of pie, if he'd get rid of NO_x for me. We met the next afternoon at Pepe's restaurant across the street from the NBC studios in Burbank. I bought the taco, and within a half hour I had a formula from Farber, who thought a muffler could be made to reduce not only oxides of nitrogen, but hydrocarbons and carbon monoxide as well. He agreed to immediately search all current literature on the subject, and did so over the next few weeks, after which time I got a call from him. I asked what he'd found out.

"The formula I gave you will work. There are several ways to handle the problem, which is simply that the formation of NO_x is an irreversible process. Nitrogen oxides will not readily break down to nitrogen and oxygen (common air). But if we pass the hot gas from a car's exhaust over a suitable chemical catalyst, it will revert to nitrogen and carbon dioxide."

"Is there any way better and cheaper to do it than with a muffler?" I asked.

Farber paused. "You could eliminate NO_x entirely by burning pure oxygen. No nitrogen, no NO_x." There was a long pause. "But, there's a little drawback. You'll have to haul a tank car full of oxygen around with you, and you'll have quite a fire hazard on your hands. You'll be driving a bomb, as a matter of fact."

After several more "taco meetings," we knew what we were up against. The reduction of NO_x was a very complicated matter involving high temperature reactions, catalysis, and thermodynamics. It soon became obvious that a new catalyst would have to be developed. "The kind we have now available," said Farber, "are 'pelletized,' which means they would break up into dust from vibration in a muffler. Sometimes, the catalyst material is painted on the surface of a high-temperature substance, such as ceramic, and it can glaze. On top of that, the lead oxide formed during combustion tends to coat the catalyst. When that happens, the hot gas can't touch the catalyst surface and the whole thing stops working."

About this time, we ran head-on into another problem — money. As Farber put it, "I'm willing to work for tacos, but my chemists want real money." We decided he should write a letter, outlining his proposal to the Department of

Health, Education and Welfare, which has responsibility for combating air pollution on a federal level. We hoped they might support Farber's work with a few thousand dollars. Off the letter went to HEW. The answer came back about three months later. They had shipped Farber's letter off to HEW engineers in Ohio, for "evaluation."

We decided that the automobile industry's ten-year estimates might be accurate, if we worked through the government. Time was too important to waste on interminable governmental red tape. Farber decided to look for private investors — which he soon found. A new California corporation, Anti-Pollution Corporation of America (Antipol), was established, which Farber now heads, and a contract was let to his laboratory, Space Sciences, Inc., to begin development of a new double-chamber catalyst muffler.

We soon found that the catalyst would have to be produced in Farber's laboratory. When he approached a large chemical company, he was told development of a catalyst to his specifications would require several million dollars and two years lead time. The disgusted Farber returned to his lab and hired several key scientists, all with advanced degrees in physics, physical chemistry, and chemical engineering. Within weeks the new catalyst was taking shape as various formulas were tested.

Each of the muffler's two chambers would handle a different job; one would get rid of hydrocarbons and monoxide, the other reduce NO_x. The devices to control hydrocarbons and monoxide, installed by Detroit, would be thrown away, since they would no longer be needed. A Chevrolet 1968 model 327 engine was purchased new, to be used for testing the efficiency of the new muffler. In the process, some interesting knowledge was gained about the alteration of the engine by the auto makers in their attempt to reduce pollutants pouring from the exhaust. "The devices installed by Detroit have caused the NO_x to increase two or three times what it would normally be without the devices," Farber told me. "The engine is literally running 'out of tune' when it leaves the factory. The carburetor jets have been enlarged, and they've added more air to the fuel mixture."

As the work on the new catalyst progressed, a top rocket-engine designer was brought in to round out the team. He was given a contract to design a muffler to contain the catalysts. It should, Farber insisted, take more shock and vibration than any car would ever be likely to give it, and in addition, trap lead from the combusted fuel and hold it inside instead of spewing it into the street."

One day, I got the call I was waiting for.

"I've got the muffler," crowed Farber. "It looks like it was built in a submarine works . . . but it's a muffler. I don't think we could break it with sledge hammers!"

Installed in the new muffler from the "submarine works," the catalyst's first tests in the laboratory were spectacular. It reduced NO_x so well that Farber was having trouble finding any trace, even when he checked NO_x on the super-sensitive mass spectrometer. After months of laboratory experiments, he was ready for a test on a real car.

Farber telephone, "You're not gonna believe this. Not one of these high-priced chemists knows which end of a wrench to put on a bolt. We're taking the whole thing up to a muffler shop."

At the muffler shop, an astonished mechanic took one look at the shiny steel object and blurted: "What the hell is *that?*"

"*That,*" said Farber, defensively, "is a muffler."

"Oh. I shoulda known. I get you hot-rodders in here all the time." The muffler was installed.

At this writing, the first muffler, installed on a panel truck, has logged 8,700 miles on premium-leaded fuel. It is still reducing NO_x, hydrocarbons, and carbon monoxide to points well below the strict standards projected for the State of California in 1975.

Late in 1969, a second unit with an improved catalyst was installed on a 1969 Chevrolet with a 350-cubic-inch-displacement engine, and delivered to Stanford Research Institute for an independent check of its ability to reduce NO_x. Results were stunning. At fifty miles per hour the engine (*with* Detroit antismog devices, but *without* Farber's muffler) was emitting between 4,000 and 5,000 parts per million NO_x. When the muffler was installed, the NO_x dropped to 1,080 parts per million. Finally, the Detroit devices were removed from the engine and the muffler alone was tested. The NO_x immediately fell to 280 parts per million! Over the full driving range from zero to fifty miles per hour, the car, operating without Detroit's devices and depending solely on Farber's muffler for reduction of pollutants, showed NO_x was cut to approximately 80 parts per million, average!

As soon as he is satisfied the muffler has passed all tests he has scheduled for it, Farber intends to turn it over to the state of California for its official acceptance tests.

"What we have done was simple enough in the laboratory," said Farber. "It should pass state tests. It has a good chance of exceeding them, including the life tests. We have no idea how long it will last. Theoretically, you can't wear out a catalyst. The only thing that could happen would be that it eventually would become coated with lead. At that point, the car's owner would simply remove the catalyst, much as he removes an oil filter today, and replace it with a new one."

What will it cost retail? Farber feels the muffler will sell for about $30 to $40 more than the current devices on the car, which, of course, would no longer be required. He believes the catalyst portion can be replaced for about $25. These figures are based on mass production.

When the motorist removes the catalyst, he will find several pounds of lead," said Farber, "since we are trapping the lead from the burned gasoline inside, rather than letting it exhaust to the atmosphere. If the day comes that we no longer permit lead to be used in gasoline, then it may no longer be necessary to replace the catalysts. They should, under those condition, last the life of the car."

Strangely, though the muffler was described on the documentary presented in May and again in June 1969 on KNBC in Los Angeles, little reaction concerning it came from the public and industry. Apparently there is deep suspicion over solutions not brought forth from Detroit.

In November 1969, *Business Week* became the first magazine to take notice. Reporter Jim Lowery detailed Farber's new muffler in a three-page article. Letters immediately began to arrive at Farber's laboratory in Monrovia, California from firms here and abroad expressing interest in joining

Antipol in its project. The scent of success was at last in the air. With luck and a little help, Farber hopes to see the mufflers on all California cars — old and new — within two to three years.

The success of the new catalyst opens new hope for beleagued power plant operators having trouble meeting stiff new air pollution requirements for NO_x. Farber believes the catalyst is adaptable to their needs; i.e., reducing the oxides of nitrogen pouring from their stacks. "It should be easier than the muffler project," said Farber. "After all, those stacks don't vibrate, there is no lead to worry about . . . just NO_x. There is no reason why another version of this catalyst wouldn't work admirably."

If Farber's muffler performs as well as it appears it will in state tests, Detroit's auto makers should order up a round for the house. It will have snatched them from almost certain trouble in California, where meeting NO_x standards starting in 1971 seems beyond their ability. Farber's muffler could give the internal combustion engine a new lease on life. In addition, it could make life a lot easier for oil companies, which are a prime target of the public for their leaded gasoline. For California, the muffler, if successful, would mean a virtual end to smog.

Installation of the muffler on California cars would also be a big boost for government speech writers. Late last summer (1969) a battery of federal officials descended on Los Angeles to pronounce that *hydrocarbon* smog would be gone from Southern California within ten years (there's that estimate again!). They carefully avoided the mention of nitrogen oxides, for which there is no answer — at least until and unless Farber's muffler or some other such device makes the grade.

There seems little doubt that steam or gas turbine power plants will one day take over from the internal combustion engine But it would be foolish to expect it to happen for one and perhaps two decades. Even if these modes of combustion were employed, they would still require a catalyst to remove gaseous pollutants.

Alas, at this point in time, the government and Detroit seem locked to a smog cure schedule of ten years. The only hope of long suffering Californians is that disaster isn't due in five.

Lead:
An Ancient
Curse Returns

Lead . . . that ancient metal with the unglamorous name . . .
has a history filled with romance, intrigue, adventure, and
greed. Wars were fought over lead. A figurine from lead,
nearly five thousand years old, can be found in the British
Museum. The Chinese made coins from it in 2000 B.C. The
Assyrians and Babylonians prized lead ornaments. Silver
extraction from lead began about 2500 B.C.

The Romans used lead for many things — water pipes,
for instance. The Roman baths at Bath, England still utilize
lead pipes installed almost two thousand years ago. Such pipe
was made by folding sheets of cast lead and fusing the seams.
Other uses included lead-lined cisterns, filled by water col-
lected on lead-lined roofs and transported through lead gut-
ters. Greek and Roman coins contained a percentage of lead
in their bronze. Ships were lined with lead, as were cooking
pots.

Greece and Rome financed their rise to power with
silver obtained from the lead mines of Spain and Attica. But
with all the glory, there was misery, pain, and death associated with the entire history of this mundane but mighty metal.
There are, in fact, those who will tell you that the Roman
Empire fell not from the reasons established in most history
books, but from lead . . . which like power, can corrupt
through intimacy.

The ancient royalty was willing to have others die
(slaves in the mines) that they might use and profit from
lead. That particular aspect may not have changed appreciably, in this, the twentieth century.

The Romans, some historians believe, were ignorant of
the lethal effects of lead on the human system, which will
tolerate only the tiniest amount – 0.5 to 0.8 part per million
of blood. Anything above that constitutes classical lead poisoning, which can cause brain and nervous-system damage
and death. The above theory has it that the Romans, because
of their constant exposure to lead in food, water, and wine,
ingested the metal in such amounts that they suffered illness
and brain disfunction leading to their fall from greatness.

The Romans may have had a better excuse for bringing
on their own demise than modern man, who appears to be
getting the same results from lead – not from ignorance,
which can be excused, but from greed, which cannot.

The first warning signs that we may be condemning vast
numbers of our citizens to illness, impairment, and death
from lead poisoning came in 1965 in geochemist Dr. Claire C.
Patterson's brilliant article "Contaminated and Natural Lead
Environments of Man," *Archives of Environmental Health,*

Vol. II, September 1965. Patterson, in his work leading up to the paper, found that the industrial output of lead has had a "profound effect" on the "lead content of the oceans and of the atmosphere of the northern hemisphere."

By far the greatest identifiable source of lead contamination in our environment is provided by the gasoline-powered automobile, whose high compression engine demands an antiknock substance in its fuel: lead tetraethyl. About two ounces per tankful of gasoline.

The enormity of this pollution can be grasped by simple arithmetic. Multiply the number of cars in a big city, say Los Angeles, which has approximately 4 million cars, by an average of 250 miles per tank of fuel . . . or about 40 tanks of gas per car on an average of 10,000 miles annually. Are you ready? On this basis, we are dumping several million pounds of lead into the Los Angeles atmosphere each year.

Dr. Patterson's paper, considered by many to be the most important document ever published on the subject, exploded in a field that has been shrouded for almost four decades in assumptions, half-truths, politicking and self-induced blindness. His conclusion that "the average resident of the United States is being subjected to severe lead insult" immediately raised more hell than the alligator did when the pond went dry.

For one thing, the straightforward Dr. Patterson had placed his scientific foot to the civil-service rump of the HEW with embarrassing accuracy. That imposing governmental agency was on record with the view that existing lead levels in this country "are well within the presently accepted range . . . of humans and are not significant in terms of a threat of

the occurrence of lead intoxication. . . ."
Patterson followed his contention with three more
zingers:

> Existing average (human) body burdens of lead are
> about a hundred times higher than natural burdens.

> Existing rates of average lead absorption are about
> thirty times higher than natural rates.

> Under existing conditions, atmospheric sources of
> lead make highly significant contributions to ab-
> sorbed lead, while such sources make insignificant
> contributions under natural conditions.

Hopping on some other pet assumptions, Dr. Patterson
took issue with the acceptance of typical lead levels in humans in America as "normal and therefore safe or natural."
Such acceptance, he said, "is founded on nothing more than
an assumption that these terms are equivalent. On the contrary, such an assumption may be in gross error."

He argued that the average concentration of lead in
blood, 0.25 ppm, "which has been and still is regarded with
ill-founded complacency, actually seems to lie between an
average natural level of about 0.002 ppm and an acute toxic
threshold of 0.5 to 0.8 ppm. This suggests clearly and
strongly that the average resident of the United States is
being subjected to severe chronic lead insult."

Patterson's detailed report stirred up a hornet's nest of
controversy. "The reverberations from that controversy and
the renewed interest in lead biochemistry," said Patterson,
"brought to a close an era, lasting forty years, of the com-

plete domination by industry of the accepted medical views
on lead pollution."

To comprehend why such a furor grew from Patterson's
paper, it is necessary to take a glance backward to the 1920s,
when automobile manufacturers began to produce cars with
higher compression engines that required higher octane fuels
to keep them from "pinging" or knocking." Last summer I
talked with Dr. Patterson about lead in gasoline, most of
which lead is supplied to oil companies by the Ethyl Corporation. His words are worth the reading.

Q.   How were the "safe" standards for lead established?

A.   They were determined almost entirely by one man,
working for the Ethyl Corporation — Robert Keyhoe. Robert
Keyhoe is a doctor who was hired by the Ethyl Corporation
in the 1920s to help defend the practices of the corporation
when they were putting lead tetraethyl antiknock compound
on the market. The product poisoned a lot of people at the
time. You see, lead tetraethyl is a deadly poison in pure
form. You spill it on your skin, you'll die . . . it's a horrible
death, because two or three days later, it gets to your brain
and then it's like rabies.

Anyway, they had a series of these poisonings and it got
into the papers, and there was a big hullabaloo. The Ethyl
Corporation was selling it, you see, and there hadn't been a
peep out of the Public Health Service . . . not a word. But the
newspapers brought all this pressure, and the legislature
jumped on the Health Department, which then formed a
committee to investigate — this was in 1924. They then made
regulations that very carefully protected the health of the
people who were *manufacturing* the poison.

That's the classic role of the Health Department — to protect the industrial workers in the plants, to make sure they can still punch the clock and not sue the company. And this evolved from back at the turn of the century, when the Health Department first grew. It had an industrial health aspect. I'm not talking about malaria, or typhoid fever, or anything like that — that's another aspect — but their relationship with industry has been one of protecting the workers in the plants.

There has never been, at any time, the consideration for the consumer. Anyway, after getting the U.S. Public Health Service to set up these methods for manufacturing these poisons without catastrophic hazard to the workers, then they [Ethyl Corporation] went ahead. Late in the 1950s there was a review, because it had been decided you couldn't put more than a certain amount of lead in the gasoline per gallon. Now this was not a law — it was just a gentlemen's agreement. The auto companies were asking for more lead in the gasoline for the higher compression engines. So the committee said "O.K., we've reconsidered, and you can put in more, because we've decided it won't hurt anybody to put in a little more."

According to Patterson, it was at this time that the Health Service decided it had not been determined whether lead alkyls had increased the body burdens of lead in people. Subsequently, the Health Service, the oil companies, and the California Department of Public Health held a cooperative study, along with the lead industries. Their report was criticized by Patterson for "refusing to recognize . . . that lead alkyls had elevated the body burdens of lead and the concentrations of lead in the blood of urban Americans, and that existing levels of lead contamination in people were causes of alarm – not complacency."

In 1966, Patterson asked the Governor of California to direct the State Department of Public Health to re-evaluate its position. Says Patterson: "They issued such a report in 1967, in which they reversed their earlier position on the same data and explicitly recognized that lead alkyls are the source of lead in the urban atmosphere, and that lead concentrations in the blood of people living in cities are elevated as a consequence.

"The petroleum and lead alkyl industries, in referring to the 1965 joint report," adds Patterson, "take care to neglect to mention these interesting addenda."

Patterson, who takes a jaundiced view of public health agencies, declares they are "patently unable to conduct evaluative investigations that turn out to be truly defensive of the public health." He points out that in 1939, the Public Health Service investigated public health hazards originating from lead arsenate insecticides on apples. The PHS concluded there was no harm to the public at a 7 ppm level of lead in apples (a maximum permissible level still in effect). At the same time, Patterson recalls, Dr. Keyhoe was obtaining data on lead ingestion showing that 1.5 ppm in food should give rise to classical lead poisoning in a matter of months!

Somewhere along here, it should be remembered that the above – the poisonings, the politics, the scientific wrangling – all involve two matters: the adding of a substance to gasoline so your engine will not "knock," and the profits of the lead industries, oil companies, and auto manufacturers.

At this point, any sane person must ask certain questions. Is it true that there have been these enormous increases in lead in our environment? Are we in danger of massive lead poisoning across our country? If the first two answers are Yes, then we must seek to know why it was permitted. Were the industries involved aware of the danger of their massive transfer of lead into our air, water, and food? Were they ignorant, or was it a deliberate move based on financial considerations and to hell with the consequences? Such attitudes are not unknown in commerce when a buck is at stake.

One small, but memorable personal example comes to mind. When I was a boy in Oklahoma in the 1930s, times were lean. None of the people in our neighborhood could do more than eke out a bare living. The winters were the worst. The gas company would come out regularly, like Legree crossing the floes, and shut off the gas to the entire community. True, nobody had paid the bill, but the circumstances in that village (ineptly named Good Hope) were such that Attila the Hun would have worked up a little compassion. Many were sick with influenza, there was no money and damned little food. But the gas went off. My father was the hero of the situation. As an oil driller, he was intimate with pipes, gas shut-off valves, and their manipulation. I would accompany him on clandestine guerilla raids through the snow, and we'd turn the gas *on!* Electric companies were outwitted in the same manner, with pennies and luck. Perhaps what I'm inferring is that the architects of the corporate entity did not install social responsibility — a "heart," if you will. Humane considerations are forced upon them by law and/or public reaction. I know of no instance, personally, where they've happened to come, like the Spirit of Christmas to Scrooge.

Since there is no longer any question that lead can maim and kill us, let's look at the possibility that we *are* loading our environment with lead. Following Patterson's 1965 contribution to our knowledge of the metal, further investigations were planned and conducted. The result of the most recent study was published in the fall of 1969: *Chemical Concentrations of Pollutant Lead Aerosols, Terrestrial Dusts, and Sea Salts in Greenland and Antarctic Snow Strata.* M. Murozumi of Japan, Tsaihwa J. Chow of Scripps Institute of Oceanography in La Jolla, California, and Claire Patterson of California Institute of Technology in Pasadena made the survey.

Taking samples from ancient ice and snow layers, with meticulous preparations in advance to insure against even minute outside contamination, the team measured the lead concentrations dating back to 800 B.C. Their findings may finally shock a largely apathetic world into realizing the dangers we face from the incredible rise in lead pollution in recent times.

The range of lead concentrations varied from 1 thousandth of a microgram of lead per kilogram of ice at 800 B.C., to 200 thousandths of a microgram of lead per kilogram of ice today, in the north polar ice sheets. In contrast, lead concentrations in south polar ice sheets were below detection before 1940 and only 20 thousandths of a microgram per kilogram of ice after that date. The difference was ascribed to winds which inhibit the migration of aerosol pollutants from the northern hemisphere to the Antarctic.

Measurements of lead in the oldest ice layer at Camp Century, Greenland (1753 A.D.) correspond to the start of the industrial revolution in Europe. Lead concentrations at that date were already twenty-five times above natural levels, the report shows. Concentrations apparently tripled during the fifty-year span from 1753 until the early 1800s. Indications are the lead content doubled again between 1815 and 1933. The big surge came from 1933 — 1965 rising almost vertically by a factor of three. It was during this period that the use of leaded gasolines became widespread. Today, the authors' work shows, lead concentrations at Camp Century are more than five hundred times above natural levels.

The largest amount of lead in polar snows, by far, comes from automotive leaded fuels. In the past, heavy amounts were introduced into the atmosphere by lead-ore smelting. Today contributions from sources other than automobiles are minor: wind-blown soil containing lead, the refining of lead scrap, the burning of structures containing lead-base paints, etc.

How about lead in soil? It averages about 10 ppm in the United States, but areas of heavy automobile traffic reveal lead concentrations that are terrifying. Dr. Chow of Scripps Institute provided me with hitherto unpublished data on soil samplings made on specific sites at various locations, as shown below. In Moscow, Russia, where leaded gasoline is *not* used, the soil contained 19 ppm of lead. In MacArthur Park in Los Angeles, the lead content in the soil is a staggering 3,357 parts per million! As Dr. Chow points out, this is nearly equal to a lead ore.

If you're wondering whether there is any lead left over in the air for breathing purposes, the following is interesting.

LEAD CONCENTRATION IN AIR DUST – PARTS PER MILLION

Location	Concentration
Los Angeles, California	2,500
Portland, Oregon	1,500
San Diego, California	4,000
Seattle, Washington	1,000
Honolulu, Hawaii	700
Boston, Massachusetts	4,000
Bern, Switzerland	2,500

Americans today are being subjected to a massive assault by lead. Besides the major source, leaded gasoline, we are getting the metal from an endless variety of uses. Lead is commonly used for water lines and connections. We solder the linings of food cans with it, and we use it in insecticides. We eat it, drink it, and every day, we breathe it. A portion of that ingested by the body is retained there.

According to Dr. Patterson, the average U.S. citizen gets approximately 350 micrograms of lead daily in his food and water. He breathes in another 20 to 50 micrograms. Roughly 30 to 40 micrograms per day are absorbed into his blood-stream, with perhaps half of that from the air we breathe. Our body burden is an average 200 milligrams of lead, with a bloodstream concentration of 0.25 ppm.

Most of the lead we eat in food is excreted, with only a minor fraction entering the intestinal blood. Much of the lead from portal blood is withdrawn by the liver, which rejects it

LEAD CONCENTRATION IN SOIL — PARTS PER MILLION

Location	Concentration
Paris — Jardin des Tuileries	220
Munchen — Englischer Garten	158
Moscow — Lomonosov University	19 (no lead tetraethyl additives)
New York City — Central Park	539
Los Angeles — MacArthur Park	3,357

San Diego —
  Balboa Park
  Community Concourse
	
	194
	2,307

Honolulu —
  Irwin Park
  Iolani Palace
	
	1,088
	224

Bangkok, Thailand — Patumwan Circle	 1,175

Lima, Peru —
  Plaza Grau
  Indian Ruins
	
	223
	72

San Francisco — Golden Gate Park	560
Borrego Springs, California — Palm Canyon	 7.1
Laguna Mountains, California	5.6

with bile before it enters the main systemic bloodstream. Thus, Patterson says, about 95 percent of the lead taken by mouth is finally excreted in feces.

"This is not true of the lead breathed into the lungs," Patterson added in his paper. "About 40 percent of such lead enters the sytemic blood, and atmospheric lead is therefore a much more serious contaminant. Most lead absorbed into body fluids is excreted in urine after a realtively short time. However, a small fraction of the absorbed lead is retained for long periods in the body, mainly in the bones, where it acts as a sluggish reservoir in contact with the blood, slowly accumulating or draining according to changes in the rates of lead ingestion."

Patterson believes man cannot eat food containing even one-tenth the average concentration of lead in soil – which would mean ingesting about one part per million of soil – for very long without becoming ill with classical lead poisoning. Man's food in industrialized societies contains about two-tenths of.a part of lead per million.

Already in the United States, huge numbers of children are suffering from classical lead poisoning, with accompanying brain damage, kidney and muscle destruction, and the impairment of the metabolism of cells in the body. "As an enzyme inhibitor," Patterson explains, "lead impairs these cells and thereby disrupts the natural function of organs made up of the cells. In natural circumstances, body concentrations of lead probably increase rapidly with age in the child and then increase more slowly in the adult."

He feels that we have a "standing stock" of about 50,000 children in America suffering from lead poisoning, "and that may be a gross underestimate." Recent articles on the subject have mentioned the possibility of up to 400,000 children being poisoned — mostly as a result of eating the lead paint peeling from walls in ghetto areas. Only about 4 or 5 percent of such children are treated.

Lead poisoning is difficult to detect in the beginning stages. When detected and treated, the victims sometimes escape serious damage and are left with perhaps minor damage. We have several thousand — half of those treated — who will be handicapped the rest of their lives with brain damage or other afflictions. Annually, about 175 to 200 die.

In the concluding statements of his now famous article, Patterson envisions a frightening spectre of a world where brain impairment becomes widespread from lead. "The course of human events is determined by the activities of the mind," Patterson notes. Intellectual irritability and dysfunction are associated with classical lead poisoning, and it is possible — and in my opinion probable — that similar impairments on a lesser but still significant scale might occur in persons subjected to severe chronic lead assault."

According to Patterson, experiments on animals in recent years indicate that "pathologic and histologic changes of the brain and spinal cord, together with functional shifts in the higher nervous activity, are induced by exposures to atmospheric lead concentrations corresponding to those exposures now experienced by dwellers in most large American cities."

If the lead, oil, and automobile industries cannot be induced to eliminate lead tetraethyl from gasolines by prevailing upon them to exercise a little social responsibility in the name of the public health or to consider the simple logics of economics — no customers, no profits — then perhaps the thought of a mentally incapacitated individual in a position of national importance; i.e., a general of the Strategic Air Command, would give them pause for thought. Lead cannot be depended upon to respect an individual for his station in life. The damages it can create can affect kings and presidents, as well as the rest of us commoners. If it affects the wrong one, then there may shortly be no one.

Mind you, the banishing of lead from the gasoline sold in our country need not send the oil tycoons into gushers of grief and gloom. There can yet be a ray of sunshine for those leaden skies. I think these petroleum pontifs would be quick to agree that their attachment to this metal is not some Marner-like phobia calling for fondling of ingots late at night in their board rooms. Nope, it's the buck again.

Back in the 1920s, when the need for a fuel that would burn smoothly in Detroit's higher-powered motors came about, the oilmen were faced with a problem. Either sophisticate their refineries to produce a higher-grade gasoline, or buy an additive (lead) that would keep the refineries static and make the fuel behave in the bargain. The additive approach had an element that the oil chiefs found appealing. It would simplify marketing, since they would not have to worry about refinery production ups and downs and could buy just as much of the lead as needed for the gasoline sold, no more. The decision was more fiscal than mental. Nowhere, as far as I could find, is there any written indication whether any thought was given to the effects of lead. It will be written later, I imagine, in that great annual report in the sky.

At any rate, we could hardly expect the oil companies to redecorate all those refineries at this late date. The cost, I admit, would be mighty steep.

One answer to the problem has been suggested by — of all people — the farmers, says Dr. Patterson. Oregon wheat farmers and California corn growers believe they could get the lead out by providing alcohol as an additive to replace lead. Alcohol in gasoline would control engine "knock" just as well as lead, but without the accompanying worry of fouled spark plugs and engines. Racing cars run on alcohol fuels, it should be remembered.

Those farmers have a foxy plan. They would like the government to construct alcohol stills, purchase the carbohydrate portion of their wheat at cost, and convert it to alcohol — at no extra cost to the motorist. This would pay for the wheat, finance the stills, and the government would come out even — a happy situation unfamiliar to it.

Following along, the farmers would keep the protein portion of the wheat, which would be sold as a feed concentrate. It is, perhaps a way to have our cake (wheat) and eat it, too. We might even be able to go exotic, and instead of "regular" and "ethyl" we could order up white, wheat, or even rye. California farmers, who produce more farm products than farmers in any other state, could grow corn like crazy. And corn provides even more alcohol than wheat. Other farmers across the nation would more than likely fall in love with the whole idea. The surplus problem in agriculture, regarding these two commodities, would vanish. All that land farmers are paid to *not* plant could come into use.

But wait. What about Ethyl Corporation? Well, according to its 1968 report, the firm is doing well in many other fields, including paper, petroleum, plastics, aluminum, and research. It is even involved, appropriately enough, in studies of automotive exhaust pollutants. Getting rid of lead tetraethyl should make the latter work go easier.

Air pollution officials and government leaders, who have ignored the lead problem so successfully that there isn't even a requirement for lead reduction in current or proposed standards for vehicle emissions, can simply forget that problem once the lead is out of gasoline. Auto manufacturers should be happy about the prospect of cleaner engines, as well as one less battle with a growing number of antipollutionists. They might even use it as a selling point.

In all history, no country has been so pioneering, aggressive, and energetic as America. We all grew up on one clarion battle cry: GET THE LEAD OUT! That ain't a half-bad idea.

WHY IT HURTS TO BREATHE

(Being a partial list of the stuff you're inhaling)

NITROGEN OXIDES   Produced by any high-temperature process, such as the automotive engine, power-generating plants, or even the cigarette. Upon leaving the exhaust and reaching open air and sunlight it converts to nitrogen dioxide, four times more toxic, and causes the rusty brown color in smog. So far, man has not been able to control nitrogen oxides, although a breakthrough may come soon.

HYDROCARBONS   A compound containing hydrogen and carbon. Major source: the automobile engine. Some types of hydrocarbons (there is a wide variety) have produced cancer in laboratory animals. Devices installed on cars have succeeded in reducing the amounts emitted, but as a result have quadrupled the amount of nitrogen oxides, which are generally considered to be more dangerous.

CARBON MONOXIDE   Odorless, colorless, poisonous gas. Produced by burning of gasoline in automobile engine. In high concentrations it is lethal. In lower concentrations, such as found in heavy traffic, can be dangerous, causing dizziness, headache, etc.

LEAD   Recent studies show enormous increase in lead in our environment. Chief source: lead alkyls, tetraethyl in gasoline as antiknock additive. Cumulative in bone structure of humans. Can affect brain, central nervous system.

SULFUR DIOXIDE   A heavy gas produced from burning fuels such as coal and oil. Irritating to humans, can damage lung tissues. High levels of sulfur dioxide were evident in the killing smogs described elsewhere in this book.

FLUORIDES   Poison, cumulative in the human system, is by-product of the manufacture of fertilizer, aluminum, and steel. Causes death and crippling of animals, heavy damage to vegetation. Is often used as a rat poison, and in municipal water supplies as a tooth-decay preventive.

AND MANY OTHERS   including carbon, pesticides, herbicides, insecticides, ozone, beryllium, cadmium, arsenic, asbestos, etc. Some float around, others settle on the ground or in your eyes or lungs.

H₂0 and Other Unknowns

Last April, a Pasadena resident drew a glass of water from the tap in his home — and promptly gagged. The water was alive with what appeared to be *worms!* By the time he could telephone his complaint to the water department, a lot of other residents were beginning to light up the city switchboards. They too had wormy water.

A statement was quickly issued through the local newspaper, the *Pasadena Star-News,* to settle the fears of water users. City Water and Power Department general manager John Behner assured the Pasadena citizens that what they were seeing in their water was not worms, but "midge fly larvae." He added that the "water is safe to drink anyhow and the City is acting to clean up the problem." According to Behner, the source of the larvae was the Arroyo Seco stream bed, which flows into the Windsor reservoir.

Behner said new filters would be installed at the stream

intake, but he told the *Star-News* it might be several days
before the job of eliminating the larvae-laden water from the
system could be completed. He said water from the stream-
bed was being diverted, but the larvae were already in the
system, which would have to be flushed and the reservoir
emptied to eliminate the problem.

In the interim, the water official said, "trout which live
on the larvae have been ordered and will be planted near the
intake." Apparently, the idea was to have the fish finish up
whatever larvae leftovers the Pasadena folks couldn't consume.

This story does one thing, it shows that science and
technology have gone off and left me behind – probably
along with a lot of other people in this country. I don't even
understand the new scientific terms . . . such as midge fly
larvae. Heck, when I was a kid, everybody went around
calling those worm-like things *maggots,* when all the time
those were *larvae* in the garbage cans! We didn't dream they
were good to eat. It's a whole new world.

I don't mean to pick on Pasadena. It has a lot to boast
about, including the Rose Bowl and one of the world's most
advanced scientific institutions, California Institute of Technology. And it probably has one of the best and most
modern water-treatment plants in America. All this being
true, it makes one wonder about the less affluent towns. If
Pasadenans are munching maggots, what's the menu elsewhere?

Some other people, experts on water quality, are wondering the same thing. Dr. Roger O. Egeberg, assistant secretary of the U.S. Department of Health, Education, and Wel-

fare, told a group of conservationists recently that the drinking water in urban and rural areas is of unknown quality, and added that approximately 58 million Americans living in 19,000 communities are served by water supplies not covered by the public health standards.

Dr. Egeberg's concern is more than warranted, according to the preliminary results of a government survey of drinking water. Charles C. Johnson, Jr., administrator of the U.S. Consumer Protection and Environmental Health Service, announced the first findings, which indicate a bacteria level in excess of government standards, along with a "high frequency of occurrence" of pesticides. The study includes tests in 1,100 communities serving more than 20 million people. The survey showed that pesticides were found to be present in 76 of 79 water samples taken.

Johnson said none of the samples were above the Public Health Service (PHS) recommended permissible limits for pesticides, but cautioned that "the high frequency of occurrence and our lack of knowledge of the long-term health effects of this class of compounds dictate the need for increased surveillance and research, as well as for increased recognition of the potential of this problem by state and local health departments."

Listed among the areas being examined in the survey are Vermont, New York, West Virginia, Missouri, Louisiana, California and Colorado. The study, to be concluded soon, may turn up material that will curl the hair of medical men and make a good segment of the public swear off drinking . . . water.

To those who travel about our country, it's hardly a

state secret that we have spotty water quality, at best. In some areas there is silt and mud. Florida and other regions are plagued with a heavy sulphur content. Some places have an interesting foaming solution which resembles dishwater. In my town of Northridge, California, the tap water often appears to have been strained through gym socks.

Swimming pool owners wise up quickly to water quality. When we filled our pool with a hose from our tap, we found we couldn't see past a depth of six inches. It took several days of heavy acid and chlorine treatments to clear the water. Afterward, it looked better than the stuff we had been drinking, and it smelled and tasted better too. With a natural instinct for hygiene which seems to exist more strongly in animals than humans, our cats and dog promptly gave up their ration from the Los Angeles City Department of Water and Power and subsequently sipped from the pool.

Only very recently have we begun to take a more than casual look at our water supplies. Most of us assume that water is properly "treated" before we drink it. Yet, it is becoming painfully obvious that far too little attention has been paid to a substance that is second only to air in maintaining life. Each year we sustain ourselves on perhaps a ton of water per person, through drink or food. And over two-thirds of the human body is made up of water, a loss of two-tenths of which will result in a miserable, painful death.

Water, H_2O, (two atoms of hydrogen to one of oxygen), is absolutely essential to all forms of life and all manner of activities. We depend upon it for recreation, for agriculture, for cooling or heating, for generating power, and for performing a thousand other tasks, including the de-griming of small boys. Our heightened attention to our drinking water is a spin-off of our deepening concern, as the population spiral continues, over the amount, use, and quality of all water in the United States. As clear, clean water becomes harder to find, as pollution becomes a common sight, we naturally begin to ponder: Just how drinkable is this liquid? Can we trust the supply we get, and the people who provide it? Are they doing their job? These are valid questions — ones which we discussed with a water expert, a man not connected with the government.

Harold Koenig, president of Ecological Science Corporation, does not drink water in Los Angeles, New York or most other urban centers. He doesn't trust it. He drinks fruit juice when away from home — and then only if he can be assured it has not been reconstituted with water of uncertain character. We determined why in the following interview.

Q.   Mr. Koenig, why are we having trouble with our drinking water in this country?

A.   When you look into the water distribution systems in our country, you see a whole range of problems. In our larger urban areas you have systems that are obsolete in comparison to current engineering practices . . . lines that have been underground for fifty to eighty years. You see valves that were designed very crudely a half a century ago, and they are still in service. That's a measure of the deteriorating situation.

Q.   Do you think the public is aware of this?

A.   No. I am appalled when I see parents buy filters for a child's aquarium, but permit the entire family to drink tap water. There are filter units available for about twenty dollars that fit on the faucet and filter your water.

Q.   Is it really that bad?

A.   You'd get sick if you could see the inside of an old New York water main. You have scale, rust, gunk — every kind of foreign matter you can imagine. The water you drink comes through those pipes to your home. On top of that, the water may not have been very good when it started out from the treatment plant.

Q.   Are you saying the water might not have been properly treated?

A.   In these central treating plants you frequently have very sloppy practices. You have equipment that may or may not be in use. You have operators that are relatively low skilled, that are not well motivated, that are not policed. Many of them, in short, don't give a damn whether the water gets treated or not.

Q.   You spoke of sloppy practices. What did you mean?

A.   Well, for instance, there will come a time when some guy forgets to turn the chlorinator on, or they'll run out of chlorine. It's too dirty a job to hook up another bottle of chlorine — and too hazardous. He decides to let the next guy do it, and they keep passing the buck, and they never do it.

Q.   Do you mean there are cases where treatment plants are not treating the water?

A.   Sure. That happens. I know of a town — it was in the South, but it could have been anywhere — and this town was required to have chlorine in the water. They once had a chlorinator in the plant, but something went wrong. It leaked

and one of the operators got a dose of chlorine. Once that
happens you never get them back in the plant again! Anyway, they sent the equipment back to the factory to have it
reworked to find the error. Four years later, somebody
finally called the factory. The man at the factory said, 'Yeah,
we got it back here. Didn't know you were in a hurry for it.'
They never followed up, never policed it, and that community got untreated water for a four-year period. Here the
manufacturer was as much at fault as the water plant. Some
manufacturers don't give a damn about the equipment. It
takes a very aggressive company, and it takes confident,
mechanically oriented operators at the water plant to be sure,
firstly, that the equipment is functioning as designed and,
secondly, to know what it's doing.

Q.   Is the water being treated effectively when it *is*
treated?

A.   If you have continuing shots of chlorine – a heavy
residual chlorine – you will kill millions of bacteria that are
pathogenic to human beings, even the bacteria in these old
distribution systems. However, chlorine will not kill them all
and it can't touch some of the viruses that are in there. Some
of these viruses are more severe than any physician would
like to admit, because they originate in animals. Did you ever
stop to think where the excrement from dogs, cats, horses,
cattle goes in New York or Los Angeles? It gets flushed down
the sidewalks, into the sewer systems, is picked up, and eventually gets thrown back into our ground water – from which
we draw water to run through the treatment plant and into
our homes!

Q.   Do treatment plants treat for viruses at all?

A.   They make no effort to get rid of viruses. They don't even sample that water to find out how bad it is.

Q.   Are there many treatment plants that do check for viruses?

A.   I'd be hard pressed to tell you one.

Q.   Why don't they check?

A.   For one thing it's very expensive. For another, they don't know what to look for. They simply have no idea of the intermeshing from all sources. There are excessive nuclides, the residual part of nuclear wastes, that get into cooling waters and eventually get dumped out; there are all kinds of residual poisons, herbicides, pesticides and the like, which are terrible on the human system from a cumulative standpoint.

And this is the problem people aren't focusing on. What is the cumulative effect? Sooner or later we're going to find people waking up in the morning with an elbow gone — *physically gone!* And the cause? The operator running the fluorine dosage went to sleep! It doesn't take much more of a shot above what is pretty well recognized as an acceptable level to get you in the same position as the people in one of the African countries who have been drinking high-fluorine-content water. After ten years their bones just fall apart and disintegrate — and these are documented medical history.

Q.   Many communities are adding fluorides to their water supplies as a means of preventing tooth decay. In your opinion, can this substance be metered as accurately as it must be for safety?

A.   Well . . . you can meter it, but it's expensive to do it to the degree of accuracy you ought to have. What most

plants do is use some simple correlation that indicates how
much fluoride is present in the water. It's the same with
bacteria tests: they don't run bacteria tests, they check how
much chlorine [there is] because, they say, if a certain amount
of residual chlorine is present, then that will kill most of the
bacteria. Fact is, we *don't know.* Fact is, bacteria exposed to
something that works hard on them find ways to grow
tougher strains. Thus, what was a good correlative tool ten
years ago isn't so good today.

It's just like when you are metering a fluid. You take an
orifice meter and you correlate the volume on the basis of
volume and pressure parameters, which at best are plus or
minus ten percent. If the orifice plate gets a little sharper,
then it's plus or minus twenty percent. All things that you
inject — whether it's fluoride or chlorine or other chemicals
— they have to be metered. Look at the manner in which
they are metered; how many actual, positive measurements?
Damn few — if any!

Q.   What about all these old systems. Are there any
new ways to treat our water?

A.   Yes. We should be using something like ultraviolet
instead of chlorine. Ultraviolet rays will not only get rid of
bacteria, but will kill viruses. And it's not harmful to "play
with" as is chlorine. Chlorine is one of our problems. It's
hazardous. Once a guy gets in trouble with a chorine bottle,
he'll never touch one again.

_____

As in the case of smog, man is hard up for excuses for
having visited such massive damage on his waters. He is a
victim of his own scientific and engineering bromides, including the hoary old "The solution to pollution is dilution."

That fine theory was trotted out to permit industrial and
municipal entities to dump unlimited sewage and garbage in
the rivers and lakes. The idea, however stupid, was that these
receptive and helpless bodies of water would take endless
filth and somehow magically carry it away somewhere and
purify themselves in the process.

Even as far back as the turn of the last century, we were
beginning to pollute our waters, although in a minor way.
The population was small. Still, pollution was serious enough
that the Public Health Service established drinking water
standards in 1914. Since then the standards have risen and
the water quality has nose-dived.

We, the apathetic and often unthinking public, can share
in the blame. We stood (and still stand) in awe of anyone
possessing some claim to scientific or engineering credentials.
With all the great progress made, it is still wise to remember
they have not always been right. Scientists predicted man
could not travel more than forty miles per hour because his
breath would leave and he would die. Medics once thought
that the only cure for blood poisoning was to tie a white
rooster to your left leg. In later years, there was thalidomide.
One could go on *ad nauseum.*

The basic requirements for determining lousy water are
a nose and a mouth. They may not detect viruses, but the
"experts" aren't doing that, either. If water is off-color or has
"things" cruising around in it, then it shouldn't be drunk.
But do we exercise this judgement? We do not. Instead we
are satisfied with water department "cover stories" that
beggar description.

Here's one for you . . . and I can vouch for its authenticity, because I was on hand at the time. Last July, in Washington, D.C., I arose and set forth to the bathroom for my daily ablutions. I turned on the tap for water to shave, and out came something approximating coffee. I decided against shaving. One cut and I could bleed to death without knowing it. Instead, I dropped down to the lobby for breakfast and bought a morning paper. Sure enough, there was the story. Residents had called in to report a reddish brown liquid coming from their pipes.

Harold Stearn, Chief of the Water Operations Division, was quoted as explaining that the color was created by heavy flows which were tearing rust (iron-oxide) off the inside of pipes, some of which are *nearly 100 years old*. The colored water was safe to drink, he assured the public, although that same public complained it was staining their clothes. The capper to the whole yarn was Stearn's final statement, which is equal to the best, even in Washington. He said: "In fact, if you believe what you see on television, if you've got iron-poor blood, this may be better than the old water."

Once in awhile, in a burst of honesty, these water wizards tell the flat-out honest truth and admit they don't know what the devil is in the water. Such an instance is the story out of Kelley's Island in Lake Erie, where last September the island's water supply was threatened by a green slime. Health officials admitted they were only "going on a theory that it is an algae growth of some sort." Then, so help me, they added more chlorine as "a precaution." One might logically ask, against what? Green foam? Triffid droppings? Martian manure? After doing their thing with chlorine, they added this beaut of a suggestion: water users on Kelley's

Island should restrict the green slime liquid to "only the most necessary uses." Like drinking, cooking, bathing, fellas? But maybe don't wash the car?

The state's health experts got the last word. They advised the 300 residents of the island that there "is apparently no *immediate* health danger." Now what does *that* mean? Don't call in until you get cramps? At any rate, the island's water turned a bright yellow-green. The beach turned blue. The citizens should have, too.

If there is anything to be learned from these rather incredible tales of water pollution, perhaps it is that Americans have a good deal of misplaced faith in their water and the people who treat and supply it. When did we decide in this country to meekly follow instructions to swallow maggots, rust, viruses, and even go along with green slime, simply because we are told it's O.K.? If *you* aren't worried about the fellow who's shipping water down the pipe, the Public Health Service *is. The Public Health Service Drinking Standards* caution that the production of water supplies which pose no threat to the consumers' health "depends upon continuous protection." They then urge that only the purest sources of water be used because of *"human frailties associated with this protection."* Amen, brother, amen. The PHS will authorize use of a polluted source only when "the provision of personnel, equipment, and operating procedures can be depended upon to purify and otherwise protect the drinking water continuously." Lots of luck.

Quite obviously, the Public Health Service does not intend that Americans should be subjected to impure water. Yet, it is equally obvious that we are. The somewhat ridiculous incidents reported here must be considered as minor in comparison to others occurring daily, some reported, others going unnoticed. A most worthwhile and overdue project would be the careful, honest examination of every water treatment and distribution plant in the United States. Such a study should not only explore the water quality, but also the adequacy of the lines and equipment and the competency of the operating and supervisory personnel. At the same time, it would seem only logical to determine the necessity and possibility of providing new equipment and methods for water treatment. With the advance of technology, our waters are being invaded by all manner of new contaminants, including nuclides and dangerous chemical compounds such as pesticides. Inevitably, these pollutants find their way into our water glass and are consumed. Admittedly, such a program would be costly, but the price for failure to take such action could be a good deal costlier.

In the interim, the average citizen should take a long look at what he is drinking and ask some questions of his local water department. When we can hold our water glass up and can't see through it, or we see something looking back at us, then it's *time*.

One of the most memorable lines in movie history is Gene Autry's urgent command: "Get the horses, Shorty! Somebody's poisoned the water!" Indeed.

Lake Erie:
Enema Territory

A lot of people come and look at Lake Erie these days. There's a kind of fascination in beholding how the hand of man has, within a relatively few years, turned a lovely and useful body of water into a putrid, perhaps hopelessly polluted, sump hole.

After a good look at the lake, most people are moved to some comment or other. The scientific types mutter about *eutrophication*, a nifty technical term meaning old age, dying. The more pedestrian among us snort about a "stinking cesspool." To this writer, there was the unshakable impression that sometime in the recent past our sick world had an enema here.

If tongue-clucking, head-shaking, political breast-beating, and government reportings were fruitful anti-pollution weapons, Lake Erie would be as pure as an Arctic wind. Alas, none of these manifestations has had any notice-

able impact — at least nothing to equal the forty *billion*
gallons of raw sewage dumped annually into streams in the
Lake Erie Basin, without *any* treatment. Streams? Nay. More
like latrines.

Most school kids remember Lake Erie as the spot where
Admiral Oliver Hazard Perry beat the hell out of the British
fleet back in 1812. The victory gave America control of the
lower end of the Great Lakes and confirmed in us the right to
pollute, free of foreign intervention. We have exercised the
privilege to the fullest.

The dominant feeling one gets after even a rudimentary
inspection of the facts regarding Erie's condition is frustration — with a touch of hopelessness. It is *so* bad, the pollutants so varied, the sources so numerous, one is tempted to
dismiss any thought of technical solutions and just send for
Billy Graham.

Experts these days are enjoined in debate over the lake.
Is it already dead? Some think so. Others argue that it isn't
completely lifeless, but concede that it wouldn't hurt to put
a priest on standby, because the lake soon will be. Some feel
it can be saved, but the cost to bring it back to health would
be a heart-stopping $15 billion, give or take a few billion.
Even at that, they reason, it might take generations to do the
job. Still others equally knowledgeable about such things
predict the mighty body of water can be restored to a reasonable facsimile of its former condition within ten years . . . but
the cost would still be high — very high.

While the differences are aired, the reports written, the
committees convened, and the speeches delivered, the pollution continues. In the case of Lake Erie, when and if death

arrives, it will not be from natural causes. It will be a case of gang murder, premeditated. The lake is being assaulted directly, by industries and communities on her shores, and indirectly, by other towns and industries along rivers that feed into it.

Erie is the southernmost of the five Great Lakes (the others: Huron, Ontario, Superior, and Michigan), which form the largest system of fresh water lakes or inland seas in the world. The lakes cover a combined area of almost ninety-five thousand square miles. The largest is Lake Superior, followed by Lake Huron, Lake Michigan, Lake Erie, and finally Lake Ontario, the smallest. All the lakes are polluted to some degree, although Erie is by far the worst. Of the five lakes, only Michigan lies entirely within the United States, the remainder bordering Canada. Although Canada's boundary line splits Lake Erie roughly down the middle, pollution from north of the border is minor compared to that from the U.S. side.

Lake Erie, only a little over 200 feet deep at maximum, is the most shallow of the Great Lakes (Superior is almost 1,300 feet deep) and subsequently is the most susceptible to pollution. Erie covers 9,940 square miles and is roughly equal in size to the State of Vermont. The Lake Erie Basin, 40,000 square miles of generally flat land formed by glacial action thousands of years ago, is one of the nation's most industrialized, urbanized regions. Population in the basin is expected to be approaching thirty million by the time we are well into the twenty-first century. The growth will come in the areas already densely populated, including Detroit, Cleveland and Toledo. Industrial expansion in the basin is even greater than

the rate of population growth. All this is worth noting because, of course, people and industry are the source of pollution — pollution that has taken the once-clean-and-clear
Great Lakes and dirtied them beyond belief.

All lakes are subject to aging — eutrophication. Under
natural conditions, it takes a long, long time — thousands of
years. With the help of man, it comes easily within a human
life-span. It has been estimated that Lake Erie's eutrophication process has been so accelerated by our pollution of the
lake proper and the streams which empty into it, that we
have added fifteen thousand years to its age in the last half
century.

Because pollution is so widespread, almost everyone has
witnessed eutrophication of a lake or stream. Who has not
heard someone wistfully recall a lake or stream that was a
favorite swimming hole in his youth, but has since become a
reeking eyesore? Such lakes and rivers, once polluted, become useless for recreational pursuits and require much more
extensive and expensive treatment before they can be made
fit for drinking water. Youngsters growing up in this environment often take little notice of the situation. They have
known no time when the waters were sweet and clear. Filth,
to them, is the norm.

The symptoms of eutrophication or aging are easy to
spot, even for the layman. While water in good condition is
clear and blue, eutrophication brings on discoloration and
turpidity. It *looks* dirty. Algae growth increases, piling up
along shorelines and covering the water with a greenish slime.
Fishing becomes pointless. Game fish disappear to be replaced by trash varieties. Even the blind can detect polluted

waters through the smell of rotting aquatic plants and dead
fish.

All of the above symptoms and more are plainly evident
in Lake Erie and in areas of the other Great Lakes and their
tributary streams. Two things are important to remember
here: it didn't have to happen; and it can get rapidly worse
unless we take immediate and effective action on a massive
scale. That action must come from government and industry,
which must be pushed, shoved, nagged and legislated into
doing what must be done — by us, the general public. It
hardly seems necessary to point out that both industry and
government — at all levels — have done a miserable job of
controlling pollution. Industry needs water in enormous
quantities, using it in countless ways to clean, cool, and
process. In the past, most firms have taken the water from
rivers or lakes, used it for whatever purpose, and dumped it
back into the receiving body from which it came — filled
with acid, oil, various chemicals, or garbage. Sometimes, it is
sent back at high temperature, having been used as a coolant.
Industry, for the most part, didn't give a damn about the
quality of the water it discharged. It is doubful that many
company staff meetings in the past have centered around the
stuff the plant was tossing back into the lakes and rivers.
Where laws existed to control such behaviour, few were
enforced. Government enforcement was and is notoriously
limp-wristed when faced with standing up to the barons of
business. When some sort of action was taken, industry
generally preferred paying the nickel-and-dime fine than
installing water-purification equipment. It was cheaper, and
after all, the first order of business is to put and keep as

many bucks as possible in the till.

The above is not to intimate that industry alone has polluted our waters. For sheer volume of pollutants, industry is often out-pointed by the towns and cities, many of which put their raw sewage directly into the streams. Others give the material "preliminary" treatment. This amounts to passing the effluent through a screen. While it may have some aesthetic value; i.e., breaking big pieces into little pieces and trapping paper and rags, etc., this technique is more important to the conscience of the offending municipality than to the stream which receives the sewage. The city can at least state that it is providing treatment. Perhaps no one will ask what kind.

The disease that results from our wastes pouring into the waterways has a scientific name that sounds curiously like a marquee on a health food store: nutritional overenrichment. The acids, oils, refuse, and manure we release into our water become a type of fertilizer, the nutrients acting to hypo the growth of aquatic plants, causing an explosion of overproduction. The principal agents are nitrogen and phosphorus.

Algal growth has become a problem in lakes throughout the world, as the amount of nutrients in the water continues to rise. Algae clog municipal water-treatment-plant filters, create scum on the surface of lakes, and clutter beaches with tons of rotting, foul-smelling vegetation. In Lake Erie the concentration of phosphorus, according to government reports, has risen to more than twenty times the amount needed — and is still increasing. Left unchecked, the build-up of fertilizers pouring into waters already dangerously overloaded with nutrients will turn the lake into a thick, swampy organic graveyard.

The rape of Erie has been accomplished in a remarkably short time. The lake had reached its full maturity at the turn of the century, when it was an ideal body of water and the most valuable of the Great Lakes. Even forty years ago studies showed no serious shortage of oxygen on the lake bottom. Today, about 25 percent of the bottom water is devoid of oxygen during summer months, and the extent of this depletion and the length of the periods during which it occurs are increasing. A shortage of oxygen in water develops when a demand is placed on that oxygen for the conversion of organic materials to inorganic matter. This is called *biochemical oxygen demand* (BOD).

The U.S. Department of the Interior's excellent summary of the Erie situation, *Lake Erie Report: A Plan for Water Pollution Control,* August, 1968, states that the total mass of organic waste deposited into the lake each year requires about 540 million pounds of oxygen for conversion of this material to inorganic substances. According to the report, some of the inorganic products of sewage treatment plants (notably phosphorus) do not, as once believed, flow out of the lake. About fifty tons of phosphorus per day remain in the lake to become cellular organic matter through reconversion with carbon, nitrogen, etc., adding to the tremendous oxygen demand.

Says the report: "Phosphorus is necessary for the growth of all green plants. Dumped into the lake, it fertilizes the growth of algae that readily convert this inorganic substance into their own organic cell-substance. Fed by this

nutrient, algae bloom suddenly and in tremendous pro-
portions in the spring and fall. The superabundant algae die
equally fast and sink into the lake, fouling it with algal organic matter. The annual BOD resulting from the organic
remains of the lakes algae causes an oxygen demand estimated at 18 times greater than that from treated sewage.
Thus, the algal resynthesis of organic matter un-does the
work of the waste treatment systems and renders ineffective
their conversion of waste organic matter to inorganic products. The fateful conclusion is that sewage treatment plants
being built today which do not remove substantial nutrients
are accomplishing little to save the lake."

The rich nutrients, including phosphorus, eventually end
up in sediments at the bottom of the lake instead of being
carried to sea. There they are trapped and the lake becomes a gigantic garbage pail of stored wastes. However, the
nutrients don't stay put on the bottom. In the summer,
during periods of deoxygenation, they boil up into the water
and again act as plant fertilizer, boosting the production of
algae and speeding the process of aging. With each passing
day, as huge amounts of waste are added to the lake, the
mass of nutrients grows. This process presents a ghastly possibility: the chance that the lake may one day soon undergo a
cataclysmic biological explosion that can virtually eliminate
oxygen from the water. Warns the Interior report: "Such a
catastrophe would make the lake's present difficulties seem
mild by comparison."

Along with the many other problems caused by pollution, overenrichment has a disastrous effect on fish populations. Lake Erie once boasted some of the finest fresh-water

fishing in the world, and commercial fishing was big business. Game fish have virtually vanished with the coming of pollution. Where once there were abundant walleye and blue pike, fishermen now settle for lesser species such as smelt. In some streams feeding into Erie, fishermen would be lucky to catch anything more memorable than a head cold.

While overenrichment is the major illness afflicting Lake Erie, bacterial contamination is a strong runner-up. The cause? Raw sewage, provided for the most part by overflow from combined sewers. The Interior Department study shows that roughly one-third of the Erie shoreline on the United States side is "either continuously or intermittently fouled by bacterial contamination." In the heavy population centers such as Detroit, Cleveland, Buffalo, and Toledo there is a resulting direct health hazard. Beaches are often closed, and coliform counts run thousands of times higher than safe levels.

All too often, the dynamic corrective action taken to combat such vile conditions as those caused by raw sewage is the placement of a neatly lettered sign which warns residents not to use their beaches, not to swim, boat, water ski or otherwise partake of civilized aquatic activities because of pollution. Of course, if you are too young to read the sign, tough. Reverse dysentary.

And how did we arrive at this despicable juncture? How is it that the Lake Erie Basin and Heaven knows how many other areas of the United States arrived near the end of the twentieth century still not potty trained? Well, it happened this way.

When we first got around to thinking about sewers in

this country, we decided to go for the European plan, which aimed at collecting, transporting and dumping storm waters in the nearest available body of water. The problem of sewage was left to the discretion of the individual. The individual went to the outhouse, the cesspool, or the woods, depending on his financial capabilities and hygienic bent. Combining of sewage with storm water for disposal was not permitted, if anyone even thought of it, which was unlikely. When someone finally gave the green light to combine sewage with water in storm drains, the combined sewer was born. Community officials took to this plan in a big way. It made separate sewers for human waste unnecessary, which was cheaper and therefore commendable, if somewhat myopic. Engineers had it all figured out in advance. The drains would, of course, overflow in times of heavy rains, but the heavy water runoff would dilute the raw sewage, lessening the chance of pollution, disease and other embarrassing things.

Although the fiscal beauty of the thing has attracted engineers and city fathers ever since, it doesn't work worth a tinker's damn. The average overflow from combined sewers has perhaps 5 percent raw sewage content, and at the height of storms, over 90 percent of the sanitary sewage overflows into whatever unfortunate body of water is chosen to receive it. On top of this, ordinary water running off streets is not exactly spring fresh.

A government report, *Problems of Combined Sewer Facilities and Overflows* published in 1967, estimated that fifty-four million people in over thirteen hundred jurisdictions were being served by combined sewers. The rest of the population is served by separate storm and sanitary sewers, or no sewers at all. Those in the latter category utilize cesspools, outhouses or septic tanks. Those still taking to the forests are assumed to be either boorish sportsmen or untutored waifs.

An indication of the seriousness of the pollution problem is the Interior Department's listing of contaminated water at beaches on Lake Erie. *None* of Michigan's beaches was listed as completely safe for bathing. In Ohio, only Cedar Point was safe. Pennsylvania could muster only Presques Isle State Beaches 2 through 10, while Beaver Island State Beach was the sole safe bathing spot in New York.

The correction of the bacterial contamination problem resulting from the emptying of raw sewage into Lake Erie and its tributaries is rather simple compared to the greater challenge associated with the reduction of nutrients. According to government studies, wastes should be disinfected, sewage should be given adequate treatment, and separate sanitary sewers should replace the combined type. The hang-up is once again the buck. It would take perhaps $30 billion to replace combined sewers with separate sewage and water drains. Even though combined sewers are a notorious source of pollution, they continue to be built and expanded in the United States. They're the cheapest way out, and they keep the local city officials out of trouble with citizens who carp over inconveniences associated with the installation of sewer lines.

Within the Lake Erie Basin, more than sixty primary-treatment plants account for almost 900 million gallons of wastes dumped daily into the lake and its tributaries. Another 591 million gallons come from secondary-treatment plants. Primary treatment isn't much to brag about, being a settling process that permits perhaps 60 to 70 percent of the organic pollutants to escape. Secondary treatment, which attacks the problem biologically as well, is better, removing up to 90 percent of the pollutants. Still better is tertiary treatment, but it is by no means the ultimate. In the future, advanced water treatment can be expected to make effluent from sewers into drinking water. Already in use in some places, this type of treatment must overcome the public gorge, which rises at the thought of the input of very recent output. Of the more than nine million inhabitants in the United States part of the basin, perhaps two million are served by septic tanks, with another five million served by the primary plants. The rest get secondary treatment.

By far the greatest municipal polluter of the Lake Erie Basin is Detroit, Michigan, which is responsible for over 64 percent of the total municipal waste discharged. The ten largest polluters, as listed in the Interior Department's report on the basin, are below:

Government figures also show that the waste-treatment efficiency for municipalities in the basin is about 50 percent. Even after treatment, the waste discharged is equal to the raw sewage from a city of nearly five million residents.

The many industries on the lake shoreline and along the banks of the streams which empty into Erie dump an incredible variety of pollutants into the water, including acids, solid materials, cyanide, oil, chlorides, iron, phenols, ammonia, grease, chrome, copper, fluroride, lead, nickel, zinc, and aluminum. In all, it amounts to the raw sewage from a city of three million people. The government has compiled a

TWENTY LARGEST U.S. PRODUCERS OF INDUSTRIAL WASTE WATER[1] IN THE LAKE ERIE DRAINAGE BASIN

Name and Location	% of Total Industrial Waste Discharge[2]
Ford; Dearborn and Monroe, Michigan	19.7
Republic Steel; Lorain and Cleveland, Ohio and Buffalo, N.Y.	14.9
Bethlehem Steel; Lackawanna, N.Y.	13.0
Great Lakes Steel; Ecorse and River Rouge, Michigan	8.7
Jones & Laughlin Steel; Cleveland, Ohio	4.8
Wyandotte Chemical; Wyandotte, Michigan	4.1
Pennsalt Chemical; Riverview, Michigan	3.6
Gulf Oil; Toledo, Ohio	2.5
McLouth Steel; Trenton and Gilbraltar, Michigan	2.4
Allied Chemical; Detroit, Michigan and Buffalo, New York	1.7
Interlake Steel; Toledo, Ohio	1.6
Scott Paper; Detroit, Michigan	1.6
Standard Oil; Toledo and Lima, Ohio	1.5
Midland Ross; Painesville, Ohio	1.1
U.S. Steel; Cleveland and Lorain, Ohio	0.9
Mobil Oil; Trenton, Michigan and Buffalo, New York	0.9
Hammermill Paper Co.; Erie, Penn.	0.7
Monsanto Chemical; Trenton, Mich.	0.7
Diamond Shamrock; Painesville, Ohio	0.6
Consolidated Paper; Monroe, Mich.	0.5

[1]Based on volume of waste water discharged.

[2]Exclusive of electric power production.

list of 360 known sources — with more than 50 percent
having inadequate treatment facilities.

The industries are responsible for 87 percent of the total
waste flow channelled into the lake and streams in the basin,
with electric power plants accounting for 72 percent. Steel
manufacturing is credited with discharging 19 percent of the
waste flow. The Department of Interior's Lake Erie report
listed the twenty top producers of industrial waste water
(excluding electric power plants). The list is reprinted below.

LOCATION	% Total Municipal Waste (BOD) Discharged	% Total Municipal Waste Phosphorus Load
Detroit, Michigan	64.4	46.5
Cleveland, Ohio	9.0	20.3
Toledo, Ohio	3.5	5.0
Wayne County, Michigan	3.1	2.8
Akron, Ohio	1.3	4.5
Euclid, Ohio	1.3	1.0
Lorain, Ohio	1.1	1.2
Sandusky, Ohio	1.0	0.6
Erie, Pennsylvania	0.9	2.2
Ft. Wayne, Indiana	0.5	2.6

As if the horrendous load from cities and industries
were not enough, Lake Erie is getting clobbered from other,
less publicized sources. Dredges ply the United States shores
and harbors, removing silt and other materials that build up
in navigation lanes. The glop removed from the bottom is
then hauled a few miles away and dumped at another spot in
the lake. The other spot is often a cleaner (relatively) one and

the net result, of course, is to spread the pollution around.

Not all waste entering Erie is liquid. Mountains of trash and garbage arrive from tributaries, whose banks are the site of numerous city dumps. When rains come and the rivers rise, much of this garbage is washed into the streams, from which it presently is delivered into the lake. Vessels using the lake and harbors dump sewage and oil. Shore-line erosion adds perhaps sixteen million tons of silt to the lake, annually, and agricultural runoff contributes pesticides, silt, fertilizers, etc. Federal installations, such as air bases, add more pollutants; and dead ahead looms the problem of nuclear power with the attendant problems of radioactive and thermal waste.

Despite the awesome problem of pollution in Lake Erie, which is the result of weak governments, callous industry, and an ignorant and apathetic populace, the lake can be saved, in the estimation of scientists. The question is, Will it? To do it will require billions of dollars, iron-fisted laws, and public officials with the guts to enforce those laws. Each day that passes without these necessary requirements, the lake edges nearer oblivion, and the cost of correction goes higher. Unless the moves toward a cleanup are made and made quickly, Erie Basin and her people may have to try the ultimate solution once suggested by a nauseated visitor to Cleveland: "Pull the chain and flush it."

Our Rivers: Dead Cats and Duck Dirty

As many another lad who grew up in the American Middle
West, I have happy memories of a special river – although all
rivers are special to small boys. As I recall, there were fish in
there as big as crocodiles (or so it seemed) to be challenged
with worm and pole. There was many a secret and haunted
place along its banks, where mother and truant officer dared
not venture. And there were rocks; big ones for diving
boards, flat sun-baked ones to dry off on before going home.

I will never go back. The river is still there, but it
wouldn't be the same. Where once were lily pads and bull
frogs the size of dinner plates, there would be green algae
scum. The bass are gone. Replaced by carp or perhaps no fish
at all. No longer clear and sparkling, the stream would have
turned sullen and murky. There wouldn't be any kids there,
either. They would have vanished, along with the magic.

My river is not unique; its counterpart can be found

most anywhere in our country. All the streams started out fresh and clean. But very few have stayed that way, because for more than four centuries man has dumped into them everything not held down by rivet or root. At first, the dumping made at least some kind of sense because the rivers' self-cleaning action could handle and dispose of most wastes. The population was small and the streams plentiful and rapid. Everything from dead cats to duck dirty went in and away. It was such an easy out that industry followed suit, as did the cities, springing up along the rivers and using — and abusing — the waters. Engineers, who professed to know about such things, anointed the whole procedure with learned pronouncements regarding moving streams' miraculous and unlimited powers of dilution. And it worked for awhile; but as we became an industrial nation, we learned that rivers were not the pollution panacea we had envisioned. Although some experts warned we were wantonly destroying a priceless resource, they were largely ignored, and the carnage continued.

As America steps into the decade of the '70s she is beginning at long last to turn around and face the result of generations of neglect — and the sight is frightening. What we soiled we must now cleanse. The job is appalling, the cost incredible, the deadlines tight, and the alternatives nil. In the process we must overcome a still largely ignorant and apathetic public, obstinate industries, and nervous politicians caught in the middle.

The scope of the problem, the extent of the damage, are discernable to anyone who will take the time to read or to look. The evidence is everywhere. In Florida, the Banana

River running back of the space-age hotels of Cocoa Beach is a mucky brown color and smells of raw sewage. In the 1940s, according to long-time residents, it was clear and pure — a favorite spot for swimming and other water sports. Today, a walk along the banks near the Kennedy Hilton is a sad and disgusting experience. The rotting hulk of an old boat is there, half submerged. Parts of junk cars litter the bank, rusting in the weeds. The slime at the water's edge is spotted with trash. Decaying algae is evident in quantity. The Banana is without appeal.

BOAT IN FLORIDA'S BANANA RIVER — Both sinking fast.

One recent hot afternoon, I stood with Dr. Roy Pannell on the boat dock at the rear of his home in Fort Myers, Florida, and listened as he talked of the broad Caloosahatchee River, flowing by on its journey to the Gulf of Mexico.

"When we came here is 1952, that was a beautiful river. A man could stand here and catch any fish he was big enough to haul in. We could have snook for dinner any time I got up the energy to toss a line out there. We even caught tarpon. In the spring there were lots of lilies, and you could hear the alligators grunting."

He stared down at the sea wall moodily. "Notice how dark the water is? Can't see more than a few inches down. We used to watch crabs crawling around several *feet* beneath the surface. Something's happened," he sighed. "We never see a gator here anymore. Often we don't even bother to fish. It's just black and empty out there, mostly. Sort of scary."

Dr. Pannell is being joined today by millions of other people across the country who are beginning to find pollution and its effects "sort of scary." But if the Caloosahatchee is frightening, then the rivers of the Lake Erie Basin are a veritable "chamber of horrors." Spookiest of the lot is the Cuyahoga, which has bestowed upon Cleveland, Ohio a kind of despicable distinction. The Cuyahoga has become the only river in the world posted with fire warnings. In 1969, it burned a couple of trestles. A government report refers to it as a "virtual waste treatment lagoon." Caustically pictured as the "world's longest, natural free-form urinal," many other pithy but unprintable utterances have been directed at the hapless river.

The lower reaches of the Cuyahoga are utterly rotten. The once-lovely stream now has the grace and beauty of a belch. Hideous gases bubble from the surface. The river doesn't flow; it percolates. A former resident of Cleveland swears that when divers are needed to go beneath the waters of the Cuyahoga, a new diving suit is required after each dip — and probably a new diver as well. The water often takes on the color of hot chocolate and rust. During most of the year, nothing alive can be found in the river, which one local citizen considered perfectly reasonable since "nothing that could live would be *caught dead there.*" Even sludge worms, which giggle and slither happily in the most loathsome of environments, have wriggled away to better quarters. About the only thing left that will tolerate the Cuyahoga or its vicinity is people.

Stretches of every river in the Erie Basin are polluted, some of them grossly, as is the Cuyahoga in the Cleveland-Akron area. Industries big and small in New York, Pennsylvania, Ohio, and Michigan have for years vomited untold billions of gallons of contaminants into tributaries feeding Lake Erie. U.S. Steel, Harshaw Chemical, Firestone Tire and Rubber, Diamond Crystal Salt, Goodyear Tire, U.S. Rubber, Ford Motor Company . . . the list is endless and so is the variety of substances discharged.

In the middle and nothern states, from Kansas and Missouri to Minnesota and Montana, waters are polluted, even though the area is not heavily populated. The pollutants here are from agriculture, food processing, and poor, over-loaded, or simply nonexistent sewer systems. Hundreds of plants engaged in activities ranging from meat packing to beet

and potato processing release wastes into the rivers of the
Missouri, Souris, and Red River basins. The rivers are asked
to receive and somehow dispose of huge loads of manure
from the intestines of slaughtered cattle. Testimony at an
enforcement meeting (Water Pollution Control Administration) held in 1965 revealed that Omaha meat packers
were dumping up to 150,000 pounds of grease daily into the
Missouri River upstream from the water intake for the city of
St. Joseph. Streams in the area, of course, have deteriorated
badly, and exhibit all the effects already described — including the predictable build-up of algae in overly enriched water.

Although streams in the Pacific Northwest are less polluted than those of the northeastern part of our nation, they
are polluted and stand a first-rate chance of getting worse
unless more intelligent usage and pollution controls are instituted. A good example is the Snake River, which flows
through Idaho, Wyoming, Oregon, and Washington for more
than a thousand miles. The history of the Snake is tied with
two interests: power and agriculture. Irrigation and the production of electricity have been paramount. Agriculture
(primarily potatoes, beets, grain and livestock) is the economic mainstay of the area. Hydroelectric plants dot the
Snake and its tributaries, and several more huge generating
facilities are on the books for construction by the end of this
decade. Private power companies, which seem to have a
compulsion to dam any flow larger than a ruptured fire
hydrant, have big eyes for the canyons of the Snake —
despite the fact that corraling a river can have harmful as well
as beneficial effects.

Pollution of the Snake is caused by municipal sewage and

wastes from industry and agriculture. In addition there is thermal pollution and the threat of radioactive wastes from the Atomic Energy Commission's big National Reactor Testing Station (NRTS) at Arco, Idaho. Bacterial contamination below population centers of the Snake Basin is high enough that the waters there are not suitable for body contact recreation. The bacteria (coliform group, from fecal matter of animals and man) are caused by the discharge of sewage and runoff from farmlands and livestock populations. Thermal pollution results from the discharge of cooling waters by industrial plants and power-generating facilities, and more importantly — in the case of the Snake — from stream flow reduction caused by impoundment and diversion of the water.

One consequence of warmer water is the disruption of the migration and spawning habits of anadromous fish (those which travel upstream from the sea to spawn), notably salmon. A government study, the Department of the Interior's *Water Quality Control and Management, Snake River Basin,* September, 1968, described an incident which occurred in 1967. When temperatures in the lower Snake River rose above sixty-eight degrees farenheit, the Chinook salmon run was delayed a month while the fish stayed in the cooler waters of the Columbia, at the mouth of the Snake, until temperatures dropped.

While in the western United States some heating of waters may result from sun-warmed irrigation runoff, the principal thermal polluters are industrial plants and power-generating facilities. (The atomic power plant discharges more heat than any other type.) These plants take water from streams and lakes for cooling purposes and return it perhaps twenty degrees warmer. Throughout the United States, billions of gallons of water are thus heated daily . . . and unnecessarily.

For years, the phrase *thermal waste* has been bandied about. A certain mystic aura has surrounded the words, implying a problem awesome and perhaps insolvable. Baloney. It means hot water that's been used. Northing more. The solution is no more mysterious than the cooling of a glass of tea by dumping in some ice cubes. The fact is we are up against the same problem we find everywhere else in the pollution picture: the buck.

It is basic in thermodynamics that when something is heated, it takes energy to heat it. It takes precisely the same amount of energy to cool it down again to the original temperature. There's the rub, for the power companies. They prefer not to use that energy . . . because they *sell* energy. Thus, they send water back into the river hot. Holding ponds can cool the water, as can cooling towers, but they are expensive. The thermal waste problem need never have been a problem, and it can be corrected easily if power plants and industrial operations are required to cool their return water. It's that simple.

If we are to put the arm on the thermal polluters, we are late getting started, and the situation is going to get a lot worse if action isn't initiated immediately. It is estimated that nuclear power facilities will be leading fossil fuel-burning generators in electrical output by the end of this century. More than eighty atomic plants are now scheduled for construction in the near future.

The importance of nuclear power in regard to radiation

hazards has been played down consistently over the years by
the Atomic Energy Commission and various government
scientists. In a recent interview with the editors of *U.S. News
& World Report,* for instance ("How to Control Pollution,"
U.S. News & World Report, January 19, 1970), Dr. Lee A.
DuBridge, President Nixon's science advisor, called the dangers of radioactivity from nuclear power plants "grossly
exaggerated" and "far less dangerous than the substantial
pollution from power plants that burn oil or gas or coal."
There are other knowledgeable scientists who believe the
nuclear radiation danger is very real, indeed, and that this
danger is being seriously underrated.

Public education on the matter of radioactive materials
discharged into our waters by the nuclear plants is sorely
needed. Information such as that disclosed in the excellent
article by Elizabeth Hogan and Richard Curtis "The Myth of
the Peaceful Atom," *Natural History,* March 1969, should be
digested by everyone, especially the AEC, which either
doesn't know about it or is studiously ignoring it.

Hogan and Curtis point out that material with a low
level of radioactivity is routinely released to our air and
water, where it can take years to decay. In the meantime, it
accumulates and is magnified up the ecological food chain as
plants and animals ingest it, much as in the case of DDT. The
high-level radioactive material is stored in metal drums and
then shipped to underground storage areas where it is kept in
steel tanks surrounded by earth and concrete. Hogan and
Curtis report that there are now approximately eighty *million*
gallons of such liquids stored in two hundred tanks. There they
must be kept sealed for hundreds of years, since much of the

material takes that long to decay. It is estimated that the amount of such wastes will balloon to two *billion* gallons by 1995.

Apparently, none of this is considered dangerous by the AEC — *If*. *If* there is no large-scale accident at a reactor. *If* there is no mistake or accident in storage or shipment. *If* there is no major earthquake at underground containment areas. *If* there is no successful sabotage effort.

Since there already have been accidents at reactors, errors and accidents in shipping, and leaks in storage areas, it seems logical to assume we can expect more and possibly bigger such mishaps and slips in the future. It hardly needs to be added that earthquakes *can* happen, and sabotage is always a possibility. Sleep well, America.

In lousing up our waters across the country and around the world, we have ignored a simple truth. The amount of water is limited. Rain and snow, which provide the water to form our rivers, are fairly constant in amount. If you ruin what water you have, you can't send out for more. Even so, *quality* is more the problem than quantity, and the quality is diminishing daily. As we pollute, the cost and difficulty of removing the contaminants increases in ratio. Some waters are so putrid they are just not worth the time and expense necessary to make them useful again; they must be rejected. While we go on fouling our nest, the demand by people, industry, and agriculture for *good* water is increasing steadily.

The population of the United States, which will be approaching 300 million within the next fifteen years or so, is using four times more water, per capita, than it did at the turn of the century. The water requirement of industry has grown even faster during the same period — up eleven times. Farmers use seven times the amount of water they did in 1900. Government estimates show the U.S. will double its use of water within the next decade.

As our numbers grow and pollution problems become more severe and widespread, many communities are having to scratch for an adequate water source. Fortunate is the town that can boast of a plentiful supply of fresh, clean water. Most cities have to put up with a product that is discolored, distasteful, and distrusted. It's an ill wind: bottled-water companies are finding customers a lot easier to come by these days as the public becomes more aware of the peculiarities of its water. Many housewives refuse to cook with or drink tap water, preferring to pay the extra price rather than trust the city supply. Bottlers are also serving industry, providing pure water in bulk for companies that require it in manufacturing. Sometimes, a company will give in and construct a treatment plant, as one reportedly did recently in the Erie Basin. The plant, of course, cleansed not the spent liquid returning to the river, but the *incoming* water, which was so contaminated it dirtied parts instead of cleaning them!

Considering the plight of our beleagured waterways, we should be safe in the assumption that our government is moving ahead with alacrity to repair the damage. Unfortunately, this does not appear to be the case. Laws, acts, and regulations we have. Enforcement is something else again. Government agencies have been shy about clamping down on water polluters. During a recent visit to the Federal Water Pollution Control Administration in Washington, D.C., I asked one official whether the government had been success-

ful in taking polluters to court. He admitted prosecution was
practically nonexistent, pointing out the government prefers
to "negotiate compliance through enforcement conferences."

I questioned him about the fact that while $1 billion
had been authorized for the battle against water pollution in
the coming year, the FWPCA had requested only $214
million. He advised that "the Bureau of the Budget tells us
how much to ask for."

I expressed some doubt about the ability of the Budget
people to accurately assess the state of water pollution in the
United States and the amount of money required to combat
the problem. I asked why the FWPCA didn't go ahead and
ask for the entire $1 billion anyway, at least as a gesture.

"That sort of thing," he said, "is up to the top man. It
depends on the type of man you have running things." We
didn't explore that further.

Since that meeting, the House Appropriations Committee has boosted the Nixon Administration's request of
$214 million to $600 million, at the same time expressing
concern that not enough has been and is being spent on waste
treatment facilities. The $600 million is still 40 percent short
of the $1 billion authorization, and woefully inadequate to
handle even a small part of our water pollution situation —
especially when it is recalled that the clean-up of Lake Erie
alone will require billions.

There may be some daylight ahead. California, which
has shown a willingness of late to grapple with its problems,
has adopted new laws under which violators could be tapped
up to $6,000 per day for polluting the waters. It's the toughest
such law in the country. The question at hand: Will the state

make it stick? Polluters have laughed at lesser fines, preferring to pay and pollute rather than install purification equipment. Few offenders would laugh at six grand per day. Of course, the California law stipulates "up to" $6,000 daily. We can only wonder how far up. It will be interesting to see if the state has the guts to go the limit on major violators.

So here we are, in the enlightened age. The Ohio isn't beautiful, the Danube isn't blue, and about all that can be said for most waterways is that they are wet. Many of our rivers are so cruddy that fish can't live in them, people can't drink from them, kids can't swim in them, and even the sludge worms spit up and cut out. In the future, don't take any bets when some guy claims he can walk on the water. He just might.

Aviation,
Not Alligators

Last year, Americans came within an eyelash of losing forever one of their priceless treasures — the brooding and beautiful Everglades National Park. The danger came not from hurricane, fire or drought, but from man.

In one of those classically mindless moves motivated by greed, blamed on necessity, and disguised as progress, the Dade County Florida Port Authority moved to construct a thirty-nine-square-mile jetport in Big Cypress Swamp, a scant six miles from the northern boundary of the park. Warnings from desperate National Park Service experts, who explained repeatedly that the airfield would be a death blow to the Everglades, were passed aside by Port Authority brass, who proclaimed their interest to be aviation, not alligators.

The Port Authority acted not alone, but with the eager urging of several airline companies, who would use the jetport to train pilots. At first. Later, the plan called for the field to be advanced to cargo-handling capability, and finally, by 1980, to become a gigantic commercial jet base. Not to be left out of any plan involving such vast stupidity and environmental ignorance, the federal government, represented by the Department of Transportation, got into the game by providing nearly $750 thousand to get work underway on the first runway.

As the story of the jetport and the impending doom of the Everglades began to hit the newswires, public reaction began to build. Excoriated by conservation experts, scalded by the press, and facing an enraged citizenry, the Department of the Interior finally moved late in 1969, ordering the construction stopped while a search was mounted for a more suitable location for a jetport.

If that makes you feel good, like maybe we've won the battle and the magnificent Everglades will be saved as intended when established as a National Park in 1947, think again. The thousands of acres of Big Cypress Swamp will become a glittering multibillion-dollar real estate prize if the jetport is completed. The fragile ecology of the Everglades is already strained to the limit by the Army Corps of Engineers' penchant for interminable canal building, which interferes with the life-giving flow of water through the swamp and the park. The jetport, with the attendant influx of people and business, would wipe out the Everglades within a few years.

North American Habitat Society president Doyle Grabarck puts it bluntly: "The private interests are not about to give up the jetport or all that real estate money involved with development of Big Cypress Swamp. As soon as the subject cools down, they'll be back again. Unless the issue

BIG CYPRESS SWAMP JETPORT UNDER CONSTRUCTION. Work has now stopped on the jetport because of the danger to the ecology of the Everglades. Plans now call for oil drilling operations in the same area.

A PANTHER PROWLS near a mahogany hammock in Everglades National Park.

A NEW BREED OF CAT IN THE EVERGLADES

goes to court — unless an injunction is obtained to stop encroaching development — the Everglades will be gone in ten years."

Various incidents indicate that Grabarck may be sadly correct in his prediction. Last summer, a National Park Service representative in Florida on a business trip decided to stop by to visit a friend who runs a small business in Homestead, near Everglades Park. On this particular day, the man was not in his store, but was attending a "meeting" at a nearby coffee shop.

Entering the cafe, the park official found his friend and several other men bending over a large area map which had been spread out on a table. The men were drawing lines on the map, sectioning off parcels of land. As the park representative watched with casual interest, one man pointed to a particular site. "I want this one, Bill. You can take the acreage next to mine."

Curious, now, the park official leaned close and then straightened in astonishment. "What in God's name do you think you're doing! That's the *Everglades National Park*. You can't touch that land!"

"Yeah, we know it's a park," one of the men grinned, adding "but it won't be one for long. We'll get it!"

After the Secretary of the Interior ordered a halt to construction of the jetport, other men hinted darkly that they would still get the Everglades, one way or another. One National Park Service employee told of a group which was seriously plotting to have jet fuel stored in the open at the airport so that an "accidental" lightning strike could cause a flood of burning kerosene to pour into the Everglades, sealing its destruction and assuring subsequent take-over by land developers.

It is, of course, just such short-term thinking — such single-minded dedication to profiteering — that has reduced America's environment to the battered and bloodied shape it's in today. It has happened time and time again across our land. Only now are the people, if not government and industry, beginning to give a damn about their environment. In times past, our country had space and resources in such glorious abundance that nobody gave them more than a passing consideration. When we poisoned the water hole, stripped the land, and wiped out the wildlife, we could always move over the hill to virgin territory. But no more.

A recent report by the Department of the Interior on the *Environmental Impact of the Big Cypress Swamp Jetport* graphically describes the Everglades' history and its current precarious situation.

The vast, watery wilderness which comprises the swamp and the Everglades lies in the southernmost part of Florida. For the most part, it is today much as it was thousands of years before the birth of Christ — an area of great peace, of solitude, of pristene silence. Both the swamp and the park are part of the same delicately balanced ecological community. The plant and animal life are dependent, one upon the other.

Water is indispensable for the survival of the Everglades and all life within the park. The amount, the depth, and the quality of the water determine the botanical make-up of this aquatic wonderland. The number and type of plants, in turn, determine the species and population count for fish, fowl, and animal.

TREE FROG ON A FIRE LEAF — The Everglades

The water supply for Big Cypress and the Everglades has come, for more than five thousand years, from Lake Okeechobee, which occasionally overflowed its southern boundaries. This water, bolstered by rainfall, then found its way to the Everglades in the south, flowing as a vast, thin sheet and moving at half-a-mile per day over the virtually flat land.

Records indicate that sometime in the dim past the Spanish may have attempted to drain the Everglades, a project that through the years has intrigued a variety of promoters — men who foresaw great economic gain if they could reclaim the region. Old maps show what appear to be canals, but no remains of the actual cuts have ever been found.

In 1881, the first detailed plan for drainage was for-

THE EVERGLADES.

mulated. Under this scheme, Lake Okeechobee and lakes in
the headwaters of the Kissimmee River would be perma-
nently lowered. This, it was reasoned, would reduce the
water level of the Everglades along the lake's southern rim.
The project was launched, with canals up to forty-six feet
wide and ten feet deep being gouged from the Caloosahatchee River to Lake Flirt, and from there to Lake Hic-
pochee and finally on to Lake Okeechobee. The Caloosahatchee cut resulted in the first reduction of the natural
water supply to the Everglades at the site of the park.

Happily, the plot to drain the Everglades and reclaim
the land was a resounding flop. However, with enthusiasm
undaunted and ignorance unimpaired, the Florida Legislature
in 1905 established the Everglades Drainage District and
immediately settled into a vigorous twenty-year program of
ditchdigging and levee-building. It was during this period that
man really began seriously disrupting the life-giving flow of
water into the Everglades. As part of this work, two canals
were dug, slicing across the historic path of the water flowing
toward the Everglades, reducing the volume and diverting
large amounts to the ocean. Still another obstruction of the
water flow came when levees were built along the southern
edge of Lake Okeechobee, a necessity brought about by drainage of the Everglades in that area, which in turn caused the
peat layer there to subside several feet below its normal level.

Levees along the lake had been poorly constructed, and
when heavy tropical storms spun through the region in 1926
and again two years later, they collapsed. Heavy flooding
ensued, with great loss of life and considerable property
damage.

In the aftermath of the floods, a federal water-control program was initiated, and the Corps of Engineers undertook the reconstruction of the levees. This time the levees held and the ages-old path of the waters that sustained the Everglades was at last blocked — with far-reaching consequences.

Because the great sheet of water that moved from Lake Okeechobee was very shallow — only a few inches deep in most places — any subsidence of the level was critical and could expose many thousands of acres. Subsidence did occur, and vast areas, formerly receiving waters now channeled off to the Atlantic Ocean and the Gulf of Mexico, began to dry out — again with far-reaching consequences.

Much of the area of the Big Cypress Swamp and the Everglades is covered with peat several feet thick. Formed over a period of thousands of years by the decaying of vegetation in standing water, peat is the protective ground cover of the Everglades and helps to maintain high water-tables by storing moisture. The properties of peat and its ecological importance seem to have been overlooked or ignored by those hell-bent to drain the Everglades. Had they bothered to read an encyclopedia of the period, they would have found a quote similar to the following: "To make peat a suitable fuel, it must be drained of its water content, which is sometimes nine-tenths of its weight."

In the 1940s, fires raged over vast areas of the Everglades. The peat had been drained of its water content. It was now a most "suitable fuel." Natural fires in the Everglades have always played an important role in maintaining certain parts of the ecosystem, such as treeless wet prairies. But with the coming of man and his drainage systems the fires took on a new and dangerous character. In early times, the fires, generally caused by lightning, burned mostly above ground. Peat will burn to exhaustion, deep into the earth, unless extinguished; an act performed by moisture held in the roots below ground, or by a rising water table. As the Corps of Engineers canals did their work and huge areas were left to bake as the water receded, the peat dried out throughout its depth. There was nothing to stop the flames. What doesn't burn simply blows away.

Apparently, peat in the Everglades agricultural area is on its way to extinction. One government report points out that "in 1912, 95 percent of this organic soil was five feet in depth while today only about 45 percent is that deep. It is estimated that by the year 2000 only about 12 percent will be over three feet in depth and 45 percent less than one foot in depth." The report notes that man has been struggling for approximately the last century to "reclaim" the Everglades, and adds: "while only a small segment was profitably farmed, much valuable land had been allowed to burn away, and the flora and fauna of the entire Everglades including that within the newly authorized national park had been seriously affected."

Water always has been, is now, and will continue to be the key to survival of south Florida's marshlands. Conservationists have warned that if the Big Cypress Swamp undergoes development it is certain to be drained. Canals will lace the area to remove water during rainy periods.

The Department of Interior's report on the impact of the jetport clearly outlines the danger of tampering with the Big Cypress, which provides water for the Everglades

National Park: "Removal of surface waters will result in greatly reduced ground water levels in the Big Cypress Swamp during the dry season. This, together with withdrawal for water supply purposes will reduce water levels to a point where much of the rainfall will be required just for ground water recharge — thus greatly reducing the total volume of water available to the park.

"Drainage of the Big Cypress Swamp then will result in a complete alteration of the ecosystem. Overland sheet flow normally flowing into the park from the Big Cypress will cease. Drainage facilities to prevent flooding will remove excess rainfall when it occurs and unnaturally dump it into the park's estuaries. The hydroperiod of the ecosystem will be shortened from the present eight or nine months to four or five months, thus destroying the ecosystem of both the Big Cypress Swamp and its coastal zone."

To comprehend how this destruction can come about, it is necessary to understand something of the environmental make-up of both the Big Cypress and the Everglades. Park Service personnel describe Big Cypress as a "mosaic of marsh and lowland forest types." Dominant, of course, is the cypress tree, from which the swamp gets its name. Also to be found, however, are willow, pine, cabbage palms and hardwood varieties, including magnolia and red maple which are found on higher ground. Oak and hackberry are present, along with wild dogwood.

The Big Cypress is fairly inaccessible and therefore has not been ravaged or completely explored by man. During summer months it lies under a thin covering of water; in the winter there are only pools and sloughs, and wildfires are

EVERGLADES NATIONAL PARK: Hammocks, grass and sky.

common. The swamp is a botanical bonanza; nobody even
knows how many species of plants grow there. There are at
least twenty-five varieties of wild orchid — ten of them not
found anywhere else in the United States — and more than a
dozen varieties of ferns. Even wild pineapple grow there.
These and other rare plants are protected by law, but the law
has no effect at all on unthinking enthusiasts and unethical
commercial dealers, who steal these plants whenever the
opportunity presents.

The Big Cypress Swamp and Everglades Park, though
botanically different, are biologically linked in a single ecological system. Within this environmental community, a
bewildering variety of birds, animals, fish, and vegetation
exist in an exquisitely intricate and balanced relationship. In
turn, all life in the area is absolutely dependent on water —
water in the right amount, at the right time, in the right
place, and of the right quality.

Park Service experts have emphasized over and over the
significance of tiny variations in the elevation of land and the
depth of the water in the Big Cypress Swamp and Everglades.
Hammocks rising on a matter of inches above the surrounding terrain create a dramatic change in vegetation. Because
the land is almost perfectly flat and the water extremely
shallow, water-level changes that might be totally insignificant in another location can cause huge areas of flooding or
drying.

The southern part of Florida has long seasonal dry spells
in the winter and spring. From June until late October the
area is swept by tropical storms, which dump an average of
fifty-seven inches of moisture each year on the Everglades.

ROSEATE SPOONBILLS — The Everglades

An occasional hurricane can deposit almost *two feet* of rain
in two days. Yet, during the winter the region gets almost no
rain, averaging only one inch in December.

As the water recedes in the winter, dry ground emerges
and water can be found only in ponds or holes. Some of
these holes are depressions where fires have burned peat.
Others are dug by alligators, which use the holes as a refuge
in the dry season. Such pockets of moisture play a critical
role in the ecological system because it is here that small fish
and other aquatic life must stay to live through the dry
season. Even here, the Everglades are in trouble, because
poachers have taken so many alligators that there has been a
sharp decrease in the number of holes in which smaller organisms can survive the low-water months.

ONE PURSE, COMING UP. Alligators, critical to the ecology of the
Everglades National Park, are protected by law and poached by people.

The wet-dry cycle is natural and necessary to the ecological balance. During periods of inundation, production of food-chain organisms such as fish, phytoplankton, and crustaceons is high. The drying period concentrates these organisms in pools, ponds and holes, where they become food for larger fish, birds, snakes, etc. This ancient life-cycle – high reproduction during the flood stage, followed by concentration of these organisms in a diminishing quantity of water – must occur precisely during the reproductive period of the predators who will feed on these organisms.

There is no better example of the above than the wood ibis (stork), which will consume about four pounds of food during its two-month nesting period. The wood ibis doesn't *look* for its food in the pools of the swamp, it *feels* for it, groping in the water for small aquatic organisms. Because of this peculiarity, it fares best in shallow water with a high concentration of food organisms. Since the ibis needs plenty of food when nesting, it can ill afford any environmental mix-ups such as prolonged flooding. For it to successfully reproduce it must have a wet period with high production of aquatic life, followed by a drying spell in which these organisms are conveniently brought together in high-population puddles for groovy groping. Other larger animals at the top of the marshland food chain have the same dependence on the wet-dry cycle.

In its report on the proposed jetport's impact, the Interior Department described a period in which this cycle failed: "Severe drought in the spring of 1965 eliminated most survival holes for small aquatic life and recovery of these populations was slow when the area flooded again in the

A FEMALE ANHINGA dines on bluegill in the Everglades National Park.

summer and fall of 1965. Consequently, fish populations did not reach sufficient density to support successful wood ibis nesting in the following winter-spring dry period and the colonies in Everglades National Park produced only a few young. With much less severe drought in the spring of 1966, aquatic populations started from a higher base, built up to much greater densities, and wood ibis nested successfully in the winter of 1966-67."

In a word, the wood ibis must be able to successfully grope to cope. Already in precarious straits from disruption of the natural water flow by the heavy-handed planning of the Corps of Engineers, the ibis and other inhabitants of the Big Cypress and Everglades are in for some black-edged news if developers move into their domain.

If, did I say? One runway is already in at the jetport site. Hot-eyed developers are ranging the perimeter on the scent of the easy money to be made if the airport wedge is driven. One glance at the plan for the jet base leaves no doubt at all as to the fate of Big Cypress and the neighboring park. Down the tubes. The decision to place the jetport in the swamp will bring an army of people, heavy vehicles, residential and industrial build-up — all with the grace of a pregnant moose in a sand dune. More canals will be built, this time slicing across the Big Cypress and closing the valve on the Everglades' last source of natural water flow.

If the airport comes to full fruition, doomsday will have arrived for the wildlife of the region, which numbers among its population a dozen species of rare and endangered birds. Some of the birds are already in trouble up to their chin feathers from DDT and other persistent pesticides. Among

AMERICA'S SYMBOL, the bald eagle, has a glorious past — and no future. It is ticketed for slow and certain extinction by DDT and other "hard" pesticides, which make its eggs too thin to support the mother bird's weight during nesting.

these are the southern bald eagle, the American osprey, the
peregrine falcon, and the eastern brown pelican.

Park Service officials believe the birds in greatest jeopardy from the jetport are the Cape Sable sparrow and the
wood ibis. The Cape Sable sparrow lives only in the Spartina
marsh along the interface between the Big Cypress and
coastal mangrove swamps. The known population is less than
a hundred birds, and the sparrow seems highly vulnerable to
any disruption of its habitat, whether from man or nature.
The wood ibis breeds only in the Florida peninsula, and the
population is going downhill fast through loss of its habitat
by drainage.

HELP! American Egrets in Everglades National Park face extinction
from pesticides.

The Big Cypress is a favorite feeding ground. Other rare
birds which figure to be out on a limb if the jetport becomes
reality are the great white heron, the roseate spoonbill, the
Florida Everglades kite, the Florida sandhill crane, short-
tailed hawk, red-cockaded woodpecker, white pelican,
anhinga, swallow-tailed kite, and the limpkin. All these birds,
say the Park Service specialists, are "already hard-pressed and
have small, generally declining populations in the United
States."

The mammals of Big Cypress and the Everglades will be
as hard-hit as the bird population — and there are at least
thirty to thirty-five species, some of them rare and endangered at this time. Included are the Florida panther, the
manatee, black bear, bobcat, round-tailed muskrat, otter, and
Everglades mink.

Add to this list about twenty different amphibians and
sixty species of reptiles, ranging from box turtles to alligators. The alligators, becoming rare except in better shoe
stores, will certainly have fallen on evil times if the water
flow diminishes. When the water recedes, they become easy
targets for man.

Perhaps the most damaging (financially) aspect of the
destruction of the swamp and Everglades will be the effect on
the ecologically rich coastal zone, a four hundred thirty-
square-mile area of liquid prairies, mangrove forests and
estuaries which receives the seasonal fresh water draining off
from the Big Cypress. Included in the zone is the northwest
portion of Everglades National Park. Its bird population is
enormous, and there is an almost endless variety of fishes,
mollusks and crustaceons that make it one of the most
diverse and productive ecosystems in America.

ESTIMATED OCCURRENCE OF RARE AND ENDANGERED BIRD SPECIES IN THE BIG CYPRESS AREA

(Source — U.S. Dept. of Interior)

Species	U.S. population (estimated number breeding adults)	No. (and % total U.S. breeding) in:		No. feeding (bird-days/yr) in:	
		Big Cypress	Big Cypress estuary 1/	Big Cypress	Big Cypress estuary
Eastern Brown Pelican	16,000	–	500 (3%)	–	Resident
Florida Great White Heron	1,600	–	10 (1%)	1,500	11,000
Wood Ibis	12,000	7,800 (65%)	–	1,650,000	315,000
Roseate Spoonbill	4,500	–	–	20,000	106,500
Florida Everglades Kite	100	–	–	100	–
Southern Bald Eagle	350	14 (4%)	36 (10%)	Resident	Resident
American Osprey	1,000 2/	30 (3%)	370 (37%)	Resident	Resident
American Peregrine Falcon	5,000 3/	–	–	300	900
Florida Sandhill Crane	2,500	200 (8%)	20 (1%)	Resident	Resident
Cape Sable Sparrow	500 3/	–	(100%)	–	–
Short-tailed Hawk	150	25 (17%)	5 (3%)	7,200	1,800

1/ Roughly Lostmans River to Cape Romano.
2/ Estimated population in southern Florida.
3/ From BSFW list of Rare and Endangered Species. Estimates probably too high.

SOME COMMON AND RARE MAMMALS FOUND IN THE BIG CYPRESS SWAMP JETPORT AREA

(Source – U.S. Dept. of Interior)

Species	Big Cypress Population	State Pop.	% of Pop.	Distribution	Preferred Habitat	Future Trends
RARE AND ENDANGERED MAMMALS						
Florida Manatee (Sea Cow)		unknown	?	Everglades National Park, Biscayne Bay, St. Johns River	Marine & estuarine	Will probably survive with protection & maintenance of estuarine areas.
Mangrove Fox Squirrel	unknown	unknown	unknown	In area west of the Everglades & south of the Caloosahatchee River.	In mangrove forests	Unable to estimate
Panther (Florida)	125 (1 per 10 sq. mi.)	100-300	75%	Sporadically distributed statewide, mainly Everglades	Mixture of swamps, hammocks, flatwoods, and sand pine-scruboak type when in relatively inaccessible condition	Population on decline due to encroachment into inaccessible areas.

| Everglades Mink | Rare — population unknown | unknown | ? | Everglades area | Aquatic habitats, swamps, marsh, lakes, ponds, bays, rivers, coastlines | Population declining due to encroachment and loss of habitat. |

OTHER MAMMALS

Species	Big Cypress Population	State Pop.	% of Pop	Distribution	Preferred Habitat	Future Trends
Wildhog	300-500	17,000	3%	Sporadically statewide (not a game animal in Collier Co.)	Mixture of flatwoods, hammocks, sand, pine-scruboak, swamp, fresh-water marsh, & pineoak uplands	Needs constant re-stocking or could easily be killed out.
Bobcat	400-500 (1 per 2 sq. mi.)	unknown	—	Statewide	Mixture of swamps, hammocks, flatwoods, & sand, pine-scruboak types	Population on decline due to loss habitat
Round-tailed Muskrat	Common in restricted areas	unknown	—	Statewide in restricted areas	Aquatic habitats, swamps, marsh, lakes, ponds, rivers.	Population static or on decline due to drainage

Species	Big Cypress Population	State Pop.	% of Pop.	Distribution	Preferred Habitat	Future Trends
Otter	Common population unknown	unknown	—	Statewide	Aquatic habitats, swamps, fresh-water marshes, lakes, ponds, rivers, bays & coastlines	Population on decline due to drainage & loss of habitat.
Squirrel — Grey	150,000	5,000,000	3%	Statewide	Mature forest stands in swamps, hammocks & around towns where trees are abundant. No. 1 small game in Fla.	Population is at its peak and is declining due to destruction of hardwoods.
Black Bear	80-100	1,000	8-10%	Sporadically distributed Statewide	Mixture of swamps, hammocks, flat-woods, and sand pine-scruboak types when in relatively inaccessible condition	Will remain constant for 10-15 years then go down in numbers from human population pressure

Species				Range	Habitat	Remarks
Marsh Rabbits	Common populations unknown	unknown	—	Statewide	Mixture of swamps, hammocks, marshes, wet prairies, wet pine flatwood, mangrove swamps.	Population at peak and fluctuating.
Raccoon	80,000 (1 per 10 acres)	unknown	—	Statewide	Mixture of swamps, hammocks, flatwoods and sand pine scruboak types	Population is at peak and fluctuating
Opossum	Common	unknown	—	Statewide	Mixture of swamps, hammocks, flatwoods and sand pine scruboak types	Population is at peak and fluctuating.
White Tailed Deer	7,000	300,000	3%	Statewide	Mixture of flatwoods, sand pinescruboak, pineoak uplands, swamp, hammocks and freshwater marsh. No. 1 big game in Fla.	Population on the increase since screw worm fly larvae eradication program.

The waters off the coastal zone are a big attraction to sport fishermen, who can go after anything from mullet and tarpon to flounder and yellow tail. Many of the fish depend on the coastal zone organisms for their food. If that food source collapses, the forty thousand fishermen who visit the area each year are in for slim pickings.

The enormous importance of the coastal estuaries was pointed up recently in the results of research performed by the University of Miami's Institute of Marine Sciences, in conjunction with the U.S. Bureau of Commercial Fisheries. The findings proved that the commercially important pink shrimp, spawned on the fishing grounds, migrate to the coastal estuarine where they find food and refuge. After reaching adulthood, the shrimp make a return trip to the fishing grounds. Any disruption of the estuarine "safe harbor" for the shrimp could, and probably would, wipe out the highly profitable shrimp fisheries, which do a multi-million-dollar business annually.

A recent study of the estuarine habitat indicates that dead plant material (primarily mangrove) is an important reason for the richness of the system. The decaying plant material was found to be high in protein — and to decay more rapidly in brackish water. The nutrient from the dead plant material is found in bays and even in off-shore coastal areas, where it is carried by northeast winds. Should the Big Cypress be drained, as it would be if any major development were carried out, the wet-dry cycle of the coastal zone would be badly disrupted.Water runoff from Big Cypress, even if the quantity is unchanged, will be much faster, and the result will be shorter wet seasons and much longer dry periods. The

SUNSET ON THE MANGROVE COAST. And maybe for it.

reproductive activities in the estuaries, perfectly in tune with the seasonal changes for thousands of years, would be unable to adapt to a new environment suddenly unsynchronized.

As if all this were not enough, the airport will create one hell of a noise problem with jumbo jets thundering in and out. While this will not have the disastrous effect which could be expected from drainage and development, it is nevertheless going to be a problem. How much of a problem, nobody knows. Certainly Indians who live in the area, as well as other future residents, are likely to make a little noise of their own when they begin to suffer the jet frets. The mysterious, almost suffocating silence of the Everglades will be gone forever. How this noise will affect the mating and nesting habits of birds in the region is not known, but it seems reasonable that they will not enjoy the intrusion and could hardly be blamed if they fail to work up any decent degree of ardor. After all.

So, if the wood stork is to lose its passion, and the nation its Everglades, what then is to be gained from this whole grand plan? Well, according to the Dade County Port Authority's Annual Report for 1968, Florida would boast an airport big enough to house the four largest existing commercial airfields in the United States (Kennedy, Washington International, San Francisco, and Los Angeles), and still have room left for Washington's Dulles Airport. The report also notes that the airport is large enough for six east-west runways, and brags that the field is "larger in size than the land area of the entire city of Miami."

Economically, there is little question that the southern section of Florida would experience a boom of sorts if the commercial jetport becomes operational. There would be thousands of new jobs created, not only at the airport, but in the surrounding area, where a business-industrial-residential build-up is certain. The economic gain would be local. The environmental loss would be national.

In their fervor to push the airport into being and to hell with the alligators, the proponents have more or less ignored the fact they are laying their runways smack in the middle of an aquatic zoo. Until they have succeeded in wiping out or driving away the wildlife, they will have to contend with it — a matter not to be taken lightly.

For instance: mid-air collision with birds. And there are all manner of birds in the Big Cypress area, and in rather impressive numbers. A flight of a thousand ducks at five hundred feet altitude can make an interesting incident when encountered by a big jetliner. If the event comes to pass, which seems more than a passing possibility, and the big jet engines begin ingesting fowl and feathers, the airlines may have the unhappy task of searching for pieces of their $20 million airplane among the sawgrass and cypress. The Interior's report on the proposed jetport studies the problem in some detail and concludes that the danger from bird strikes is very real for any aircraft operating in Big Cypress.

The problem of aircraft vs. wildlife illustrates the bizarre nature of a jetport in this particular location. It also brings to mind once again how stupidly we have acted in the past in regard to our precious environment. It is an overpowering endictment to think that almost any town of any size boasts a Chamber of Commerce, that amalgamation of business interests which aims to entice more business or to improve the take of the already existing ones. At the same time, one would be strained to find a single city, no matter how large, which has a Chamber of Environment. Even the sound of it is strange. In the past, our idea of environmental conservation has been to save two acres of greenery in the center of town on which a cannon of brass and a statue of a forgotten military leader serve as targets for any bird not yet done in by population or pesticide.

If the Big Cypress Swamp and Everglades National Park are saved, and if the financial powers behind development of a jetport are thwarted, it will be a rare thing, indeed. When nature and business collide, nature seldom comes off on top. This is not to infer that conservationist groups and concerned government officers don't protest. They do. However, developers have power, money, and know very well how to use both at the top levels of government. When another slice of the environment is lost forever, the dimension of the loss and the manner in which the destruction was brought about are usually disclosed in the form of a post mortem.

As the battle develops in such situations, the government often seems strangely uninformed; therefore, so is the public. A careful examination sometimes shows, however, that field reports concerning the impending disaster *have been* forwarded to state or federal headquarters. What happens to such reports? Many specialists down the line in government would like to know, including some of the men of the National Park Service.

In July 1969, when the controversy over the Big Cypress Jetport was building to a climax and park personnel were putting together their last-ditch arguments to save Ever-

glades, I visited the park headquarters and talked with some
of the men who watch over the big wilderness. One was Dr.
Bill Robertson, research biologist for the park. Like most
others in government service, Dr. Robertson is a man who
does his job, files his reports, and leaves political bickering to
the politicians. But like many others of late, he is a man
worried about our environment. On the day we talked, Dr.
Robertson and his colleagues were bitterly fearful that the
jetport and the accompanying growth of population and
construction would win out.

"There is more to be feared from developing industries
than from the airport," Robertson said moodily. "The jets are
only the leading wedge. The developers will follow. It's hard
to see how this park could accommodate this. And how can
we hope to stop it — here or anywhere else? The National
Park Service has perhaps two dozen biologists — that's less
than one per park in the United States! These pitiful, under-
financed poor sons-of-bitches have the responsibility of protecting the environment . . . when it's even very hard for field
reports to get out. They're hidden by someone."

Dr. Robertson's concern is echoed widely by others,
who also wonder where the reports end up. I asked Dr.
Robertson whether being quoted so openly, as in this book,
would jeopardize his position. He just gave me a tight grin. "I
don't give a damn at this point. I suppose I could get another
job; maybe even more money. But most of us aren't in this
business for the money."

In a chat with another park employee the same afternoon, the man admitted he was "fed up" with trying to save
the park from doom. "If they put that damned airport in Big

Cypress, you can kiss this park good-by. I'll quit . . . I expect most of the other men will too. What's the point in fighting if nobody cares. If it's to be saved, then you and the rest of the public will have to save it."

Across the country, other parks and wilderness areas are in trouble. Parks, even when not endangered in the same way as the Everglades, are reeling under the impact from sheer numbers of visitors, greater each year, and heading toward two hundred million annually. Hardest hit is California, even though the state has more national parks than any other. It also has more cars. On weekends during vacation season, Southern California's highways become gigantic parking lots with camper trucks, trailers, and overloaded cars inching their way toward recreation areas where they will jam together at every available site. Older and wiser campers either reserve a spot well in advance, or forget it. Others are turned away by the thousands.

Those who try to beat the system by purchasing a small lot on which to build a vacation cabin often come away aghast at the price being placed on the diminishing amount of good recreation land left on the market. On the northern California coast last summer, I priced a lot in an as yet un-developed area. I was told that a small lot would cost about $37,000. The cabin, of course, would be extra. At one time, the miles of coastline could have been picked up cheap by the state and reserved for public use. Most of the land has now been snapped up by astute real estate promoters, who exhibit considerably better long-range vision.

Much of the beautiful country still undeveloped in our nation is privately owned and highly prized. The demand for

vacation homesites has grown with the increase of population
in urban centers. Unless some of this land is set aside for
parks and convervation areas, it will soon be gobbled up,
cemented over, split with freeways or canals, and sectioned
for homes and industry. The most vulnerable locations, of
course, are those which offer the greatest scenic beauty.
Some conservationists believe national parks may give way to
encroaching civilization and the need for more agricultural
and residential land.

Not too many years ago, free trappers and other fron-
tiersmen who roamed the wilderness areas of western America felt hemmed in if another human could be found for a
hundred miles in any direction. As civilization inched toward
the Pacific, bringing with it the inevitable ugliness of polluted
and crowded cities, not much thought was given the environment. One could always pack up and move over the hill,
where there were clean rivers, virgin valleys, and an un-
cluttered landscape. Today, it doesn't work. Over the hill are
freeways, rivers of sewage, valleys of tract houses lying under
a veil of smog, and a lot of people eyeing the hill beyond.

...And Furthermore

A story carried by Associated Press out of Texarkana, Texas,
last fall described one more terrifying result of our disregard
for the environment. The city is being overrun by rats "as big
as rabbits." One hundred thousand rats inhabit the town,
which has a human population of twenty-two thousand. Few
Texarkanians seem concerned about living among the rats,
AP reported. Bowie County chief sanitarian W. E. Westbrook
summed up the cause of the rodent renaissance: "We've got
the problems because people don't give a damn."

Westbrook said a third of the city has no collection
service, so most garbage ends up in the backyard or alley. He
said open dumping occurs throughout the city, which has no
sanitary landfill. The dumps, according to Westbrook, harbor
rats ten inches long (not counting the tail) and weighing up
to three pounds. Rat bite cases number about a hundred per
year, but those are the ones reported. He said many other

bites probably are not reported. Last year, a nine-month-old child lying in his room was attacked by rats, which bit him on the neck, clawed his face, and chewed the flesh from three fingers.

Texarkana contracts for its garbage pickup service, and since a good many of the people don't pay their fee, there is no pickup. The rats proliferate and grow fat on the resulting piles of refuse. The rat population is now triple the national average. The Public Health Department tried to alert the populace to the health danger by sending an old hearse through the streets with the sign Rat Patrol printed on its side. The Texarkanians ignored the hearse as effectively as they shrugged off the rats.

Texarkana is hardly unique in having a rat problem. It only symbolizes the environmental astigmatism that has afflicated our nation — and the world — for as long as man has been on this planet. In 1970, we have reluctantly and a bit ashamedly picked up the mop and broom for a cleanup that may require generations of effort — if, indeed, we can accomplish the task at all.

A part of the problem is the insidious manner in which pollution destroys. It does not kill dramatically, and we are a nation that reacts to the dramatic. We can display casual indifference to the annual slaughter on our highways, but one airliner crash can make headlines. Before we take note, disaster must leap upon us like the beast from forty fathoms.

Death by pollution is a kind of time-plan termination not at all dissimilar to the amortized assassination practiced by one Indian tribe during America's frontier years. This tribe enjoyed turning captives over to its womenfolk, who always kept handy a bag containing a thousand pebbles. These pebbles were removed one at a time, and as each was removed, a small cut was inflicted on their victim. By the time the final pebble had been removed, the cutters had long since dispatched the cuttee to happy hunting regions.

Today, many towns and cities are being subjected to gradual destruction by their people, their industries, and their governments. Such towns appear to be gripped by economic-political paralysis, and proceed along predictable routes to their lemming-like destiny. The pattern is known and familiar. The towns begin as pretty villages. Soon, industrious citizens and their business and civic leaders decide it would be dandy if their community could attract some industry, which would foster expansion and bring tax revenues. Industry is then enticed to locate in the area. The people become employees, dependent upon the industry for income. The city becomes dependent upon the taxes gained. Commercial businesses expand and become dependent upon the revenue drawn from industry and its employees. Industry is similarly locked in to the town by its heavy investments and its dependence on a skilled labor force.

As the town expands, problems arrive on schedule. More of everything is needed. More schools, more homes, more roads. The town outgrows its sewers. It needs more and better water treatment. All mean higher taxes, and nobody wants that. Pollution arrives, as surely as the gas bill. The people begin to notice the change in their environmental quality, and they grumble. Industry is blamed as the sole villain (which it isn't). Industries fight back with the threat, real or implied, that they will pack up and move. Faced with

the stark reality of job loss and the many related unpleas-
antries, the people stop pressing and the pollution continues.

Eventually, the sparkling brook that ran through the
town becomes a fetid stew of manure and industrial waste.
The hills and mountains that once were a seasonal delight are
now seldom visible under the pall of air pollution. Homes and
commercial buildings take on a shabby, faded look. Housewives despair at cleaning chores that seem endless. Merchants
conduct a continuous war against grimy windows and sooty
merchandise. Often a foul odor permeates the town.

Finally, the inevitable happens. Young people begin to
leave the town. Industry is no longer able to attract top
personnel, who balk at bringing their families to live there.
Property values begin a long decline. In the final stages, business and industry become disenchanted as well, and the
exodus quickens. In the end, the town finds itself with rows
of empty homes and stores on dirty streets that go unre-
paired because there is no money. The village, once pretty
and popular, has completed the pollution cycle and becomes
a neglected cemetery.

One town showing distressing signs that this decay
process has begun is the once-lovely Kingsport, Tennessee.
Nestled in the mountains of northeastern Tennessee near the
Virginia border, Kingsport was described in 1917 as the
"model small American city." In later years, residents
proudly referred to their town as "the city of industry." That
industry includes Tennessee Eastman, a division of the Eastman Kodak Company, and probably the biggest single industry in the state. There are other large facilities such as the
Kingsport Press, one of the major book manufacturing plants

in the United States, and the big Mead Fiber Company plant
that makes paper. High explosives for the military services are
produced by the Holston Ordnance Works.

Older residents remember when the Holston River,
which runs through the city, was clear and clean. As late as
the 1940s it was used for swimming. Today, the river is polluted. No one would consider swimming there. It isn't even
pleasant to look at.

When I visited Kingsport in 1953 the town captivated
me. Pretty and clean, it seemed to be successfully combining
industry and people – retaining its beauty in the bargain.
When I returned in 1969 I got a shock. A familiar gray smog
hid the mountains. The river seemed much dirtier, and smoke
was belching from stacks.

I talked with people in Kingsport about the situation,
and most of them obviously didn't care for the subject.
Generally, the reaction was a nervous "they're doing something about it"; but they didn't show a lot of confidence that
this was the case.

Kingsport's slip is showing. There are occasional cracked
sidewalks, boarded-up stores, and buildings showing signs of
dirt and neglect. At Ridgefield, an attractive country club
area, there is no escape from the pollution. One housewife
wiped a cloth across her dining table and exhibited it in
disgust; it was black with soot and dirt. "I waxed it an hour
ago. It's impossible to keep anything clean." Later that
evening, we stood in her backyard and got a whiff of foul
odors drifting over from the industrial area. Her family
noted, somewhat defensively, that it "isn't always this bad,
and sometimes you can't smell it at all . . . when the wind

blows the other way."

Property values in Kingsport have seen better days. Whether pollution is a major cause as yet is debatable, of course, but one former resident recalled that city lots he owns once were bringing offers of $47,000. "Today," he grins bitterly, "I can't unload them for a fourth of that price"

In one sense, Kingsport may be luckier than most towns: it has enough power in its industrial base to turn around and start moving in the other direction — providing, however, the people, the officials, and their business leaders recognize the symptoms of decay and move to correct the problems. Kingsport is by no means in as much trouble at this point as many other communities. Experts believe some cities, including some major ones, are in such dire straits they really aren't worth the effort and expense required to attempt a rescue; it would be simpler to plow them under and start over. Rather, Kingsport seems almost typical, beset as she is by most of the evils of population, industrialization, and urban sprawl. It is bad enough when a dusty, ugly little town folds for one reason or another. It is downright demoralizing to watch the thousand-cuts process scar a town with the beauty and potential of a Kingsport. Hopefully, the people will take a long look at their town and reflect on this fact: more than one community has awakened one day to find that everything going for it went.

In the building of cities from Mule Shoe, Texas, to London, England, we have historically selected the most pleasant possible environment and then systematically set about to destroy what attracted us to the spot in the first place. Afflicted with what amounts to a cemental aberration, we lay concrete with witless abandon. Freeways, highways, streets, sidewalks . . . anything that can be overlaid will be.

California schools are notorious for their savage attack on any defiant blade of grass. Asphalt is king. Playgrounds closely resemble the Tarmac taxi strip at a fighter base. Every time I see one I instinctively look for a "follow me" truck. The reason given for children being subjected to tarred play areas is cost. Tar is cheaper to maintain than grass. Yet the same school may have a gilt-edged indoor recreation room replete with a *pool table*. But can we blame the school officials? Hardly. We did not demand the grass; we demanded lower taxes.

The tarred playground *did* eliminate grass-stained knees. Boys don't do a lot of tumbling and falling on asphalt: they'd come home in a basket. I suppose the asphalt accounts at least in part for the virtual disappearance of the ancient form of mortal combat known as marbles — with the attendant larceny called grabs, conducted at the sound of the recess bell. The honorable sport of mubletypeg has suffered a similar fall from favor. With the decline of these traditional competitions went certain valuable skills useful in later life. A great deal of finesse was required to practice the "fudge," a deft form of cheating calibrated in hundredths of an inch, in the game of marbles. An equal degree of talent was necessary to detect such chicanery, which was engaged in and admired by all. Even if you *were* cleaned out by grabs, there was always a handy frog which could be smuggled past hostile teachers and later thrust down the back of the girl in front of you. This made a success of an otherwise disastrous day. The

FACTORY SMOKE IN KINGSPORT, TENNESSEE.
"Not so bad when the wind blows the other way."

frogs are gone now, along with the grass and trees. I suppose, in the great modern, progressive scheme of things, it is a small loss. But it is a loss, nevertheless. My kids don't even know or care that I was once the champion fudger for blocks around. They haven't even the rudimentary facts necessary to negotiate trades (ten cat eyes for one aggie, twenty regulars for a taw).

It is probably true that asphalt playgrounds were a predictable happening. Very little thought has ever been given to the environment when planning any facility. The consideration was money. Beauty is relegated to children's picture books *inside* the class room. Even there, precious little has been or is being taught about our environment. Following broadcast of "The Slow Guillotine" (the documentary film on pollution), I began to get telephone calls from desperate teachers. Would I address their class on the subject of ecology and the environment? Would I show the film? An elementary-school teacher pleaded that she had combed film lists and could find not a single movie dealing with the problem. It's an almost unknown subject in the schools, apparently.

But the stark coldness of a California schoolyard becomes insignificant in ecological importance when considered next to Project Sanguine, being pushed by the Navy. This smashing idea is to rip up the beautiful North Woods of Wisconsin so that a gigantic communications network of wires can be buried there. The thing would cover up to one-third of Wisconsin — six thousand miles of cable over an area of twenty-five thousand square miles. The reason for the project: to provide an active transmission link with American armed forces in a post-nuclear-attack environment . . . in the event other communications systems were wiped out.

Conservationist groups and experts on biology and ecology are already raising a loud fuss about the project, which they believe will do fearful damage to the plant and animal life of the region. Although there is no guarantee that the Dr. Strangelove-type "doomsday" setup will work, the Navy has spent perhaps $30 million to install two fourteen-mile-long wires which intersect in a cross. If Project Sanguine, which some feel could eventually cost $10 billion or more and "turn the area into a giant electric chair," seems stupid, idiotic, hairbrained, dimwitted, asinine, ill-conceived, and overpriced to the reader, be it known this writer will not argue that conclusion. We can only hope that unlike Captain Kidd, these sailors will not lose the map and forget where they buried this "treasure." They may have to dig it up again.

Meanwhile, residents of Santa Barbara, California, stare out to sea at the oil derricks and wait for the next blowout. They have been assured by various government leaders that drilling should continue to "relieve the pressure" — although from whom was not made clear. It seems unlikely that Santa Barbara has seen the last of her troubles with the goo, and other coastlines may be in for a lube job in the future. The new oil fields of Alaska will provide the product. Huge tanker ships will haul it. Even oilmen shudder at the possibilities if one of the tanker ships breaks up. . . .

The tankers aren't the only problem. Alaskan North Slope oil fields have petroleum potentates panting over the possibility of a pipeline from Prudhoe Bay in the north to Valdez in the south. The pipe, more than eight hundred miles of it, would send over three million barrels of hot oil each week to Valdez, where the big tankers would haul it to ports on the Pacific Coast farther south. Conservationists cringe at thoughts of gouging out ecologically delicate tundra to lay in the pipe. The oil companies say they have things all figured out so the environment will come through in fine fettle. Conservationists don't believe a word of it. The big project, which may get underway in the spring of 1970, is known as the Trans-Alaska Pipeline System — TAPS, for short. Oddly enough, that's the name of a military bugle call. It's played at funerals.

In states not as unpopulated as Alaska, sites of scenic beauty are under seige by humans. Lake Tahoe, on the California-Nevada border has its hands full. The lake is already suffering from algae growth. On weekends, when heavy traffic descends on the area, a veil of smog forms. Local property owners are trying to call a halt to the building of more subdivisions, but with small success. The Boise Cascade Company, which is developing Lake Arrowhead in Southern California, is building Incline Village, a six-thousand-acre subdivision on Tahoe's north shore. Visitors by the hundreds of thousands are attracted not only by the scenery and recreation possibilities, but by the glittering gambling casinos on the Nevada side of the lake. Officials and civic leaders are battling to solve the environmental problems which are pincering Tahoe, but the casino men with the green eye-shades would probably give long odds against complete success. The Lake's permanent population is already pushing toward fifty thousand and nobody has found a way to stop the growth or even inhibit the steady rise in the number of visitors. The incredible natural beauty of Tahoe has already been marred with the glut of signs and shops and cheesy Swiss architecture. The next few years will be critical. If the Lake is to be saved, then we must give it at least as much attention as the nickel slots.

One of the more fascinating games these days is trying to picture what will happen by the year 2000, when we will have roughly 6 billion people on earth — almost twice the number today. More than 350 million will live in the United States. By the end of this century, we will be needing almost a thousand billion gallons of water *daily*. National parks and other recreation areas, already hard put to find a place for the bears to sleep, much less the people, will be asked to accommodate roughly 250 million visitors annually. As one park ranger remarked to me recently, in awe: "We'll need high-rise sleeping bags."

Facing the above, we have continued to grow rabbitly. We are polluting our water faster than ever, despite the fact that the amount of water available remains constant. We continue to overlay open spaces with concrete and glass, and carve roads to the wilderness to speed the process. What is the end result of uncontrolled development and growth? We may one day find that camping, hiking, fishing, and hunting will have become extinct, along with the birds and most animals. Nature — or what passes for it — will be available in much the same manner as a hit movie. We will wait in line, clutching our $6 tickets, for a chance for a gen-u-wine wilderness area tour. I can hear the guide, hawking his wares: "Yesiree, folks. Inside you'll see an honest-to-goodness live deer and a true-to-life replica of a bald eagle. You kiddies

who collect coins will remember the eagle! And don't miss
the live alligator . . . brought here at great expense after the
Everglades dried up. And don't worry about any bugs in
there folks. This whole place was sprayed with DDT thirty
years ago and there ain't been nothing in there since. And we
urge you to go right ahead and walk on the grass. Can't hurt
the Astro-turf. The whole trip only takes eight minutes, and
when you come out the other side, to the parking lot, don't
forget to pick up your plastic model of the Ponderosa pine
that used to grow in these parts. We *do* ask you to keep your
children by the hand. The whole acre is wilderness, you
know. And keep movin' right along so's the other folks
behind you can get a chance to see the National Park too.
Enjoy your trip."

What we Americans don't concrete, bulldoze, gas, or
trample, we cover with a stupendous amount of litter. An
untidy 3.5 billion tons of waste is discarded each year. We
pride ourselves on our nonreturnable bottles and practically
indestructible cartons and cans. Even the first men on the
Moon left some litter behind. If some alien being were to
land there later and be unable to read the signs, he'd still
know Americans had been there ahead of him. And Americans are almost defiant about littering. We will ignore signs
warning of $500 fines for littering, and deliberately toss
papers from our cars — an act seldom seen in Europe. Nobody has yet figured out why we act this way. Perhaps it is
the result of always having had wide-open spaces and few
people, compared to older, highly developed countries. Military bases don't suffer from such abuses because the penalty
is immediate and severe. I treasure the memory of a full

colonel, complete with medals and braid, "policing the area," picking up bottles and papers. He had been caught discarding a paper wrapper on an Air Force base, and was forced to spend Saturday afternoon in humiliating labor.

A certain form of public repentance for pollution past and present is being shown by some industries. One beverage company has started offering refunds for any empties returned. Commendable, even if the company *is* reaping reclamation benefits. Sensing the rising public outrage over pollution, other companies are using advertising space to describe their efforts to fight environmental contamination. Bethlehem Steel Company, in a full-color double truck (two-page) ad in *Newsweek* (June 9, 1969), detailed its programs, including acid mine-water purification at its Johnstown, Pennsylvania, coal mines, and the planting of "locust seedlings and forsythia" at its limestone quarry at Annville, Pennsylvania. However, one wonders why the company did not take the advertising money and apply it to good advantage in the Lake Erie Drainage Basin, where one federal report lists Bethlehem Steel as the third largest U.S. producer of industrial waste water. It is not this writer's aim to single out Bethlehem. The fact that it is concerned enought to do *anything* about its pollutants indicates it is more enlightened than some of its sister industries, which aren't even blessed with good intentions.

Although some of our ignorance of the pollution problem was a product of self-induced blindness toward an embarrassing subject, it is also true that information about the matter has not been widely disseminated. It would be interesting to see the result of a program which would post

signs at every point where pollution existed. Our country
would probably take on the aspect of a giant protest rally —
with placards as far as the eyes could see. Such signs are not
posted, of course, except in areas so grossly contaminated
that a real threat to human health exists. The signs would be
a humiliation to local residents and a deterrent to visitors.
They also might be a very effective means of forcing action.

As the environmental dawn breaks in the 1970s, another
danger is apparent: overreaction. Spurred by an alarmed
public (and rightly so), legislators may begin spawning hordes
of conflicting, overlapping, and unworkable laws which will
snarl progress in red tape and law suits. This is especially true
on a local or regional level. Pollution pays not the slightest
attention to political or geographical boundaries, and local
attempts to battle the problem often make no more sense
than being the only guy on your street to rake leaves. Pollution and pollutants are nomads. National and even international regulations are vital.

Industry has a valid point when it complains that one
company cannot afford to expend the amounts needed for
pollution control if its competitors do not do likewise.
Obviously, we need national laws to handle the problem
justly. With such laws, it would seem necessary to provide
inducements, perhaps in the form of tax incentives. Attached
to the incentive could be a time schedule for compliance.
Industries failing to meet the schedule, without an air-tight
alibi for that failure, could have an extension — but minus
the incentive. Failure to meet this deadline would mean
shutdown of their operations until the pollution abatement
requirements are met. The odds are few industries would fail

to comply. Barring the tax-incentive approach, industry should be required to increase the price of its products to cover the cost of pollution control. Proposals aimed at forcing industry to bear the entire load, however satisfying, are unrealistic and would only serve to delay the national cleanup. We can ill afford any delay.

Obviously, cities must be brought to bay and helped to stop polluting our waters. In his State of the Union message, President Nixon addressed himself to this goal, announcing: "I shall propose to this Congress a $10 billion nation-wide clean-waters program to put modern municipal waste treatment plants in every place in America where they are needed to make our waters clean again. . . ." A noble plan, if somewhat fiscally naive. Based on information readily available, it appears the President could blow the whole $10 billion in the Lake Erie Basin and still end up paddling around the Cuyahoga looking for a clean spot. The cleanup is probably going to require several times the amount suggested.

However, not all antipollution measures need be billion-dollar projects. The hamlet of Great Chesterford, England, hard-pressed to find extra billions for her environmental needs, took a direct approach to the problem. The problem, in her case, is that the flow in the local sewer sometimes slows down, with a resultant rise in odors. Rather than go the expensive technological route, the city fathers sought out one Bernard Berry, renowned locally for his "sensitive nose." Berry promptly accepted the position of "village sniffer" with the mission of detecting in advance of ordinary noses the dreaded flow slow. United Press International, in reporting the story, pointed out that the plan is working well

GARBAGE AND TRASH PILE UP unnoticed in the water in London's old dock area. Rats here reach legendary size.

HERE ON THE BEACH at San Malo, France, children come to play and watch the tide — one of the highest in the world — come and go. To the attuned nose, there is one more thing: the unmistakable odor of raw sewage.

and saving the village money. With his super-sensitive nostrils, Berry is able to detect odors even without lifting manhole covers. Alerted, the village sewer operators can increase the water flow and send the offending wastes on their way again before other townspeople are aware there was a problem.

Amidst all the gloom prevalent regarding our environment and the wounds we have inflicted upon it, there are some patches of blue sky beginning to show here and there. One example: Interior Secretary Hickel is working a trade of the Santa Barbara oil leases for Navy oil reserves in Elk Hills near Bakersfield, California. Another example: a water project totaling nearly $90 million has been scrapped in Ventura County, California. Why? The project would have invaded the sanctuary of the rare giant California condor, where fifty of the birds still nest. An Associated Press wire story on the subject quoted the Interior Department thusly: "If the project were to be authorized by Congress and constructed, the extinction of the condors would be an almost certain consequence. The welfare of the condors is of over-riding concern. It is unique, not duplicated elsewhere."

Two years ago, such action to save fifty birds would have been laughed off as preposterous. In fact, merely suggesting the action would have been unique . . . not duplicated elsewhere.

Timetable for Disaster

As this chapter is being written, one of the greatest – and perhaps most important – struggles in the history of our nation is taking form across the land. Disorganized, moving with more force than direction, it is a ground swell from people who are beginning to sense, with a kind of animal instinct, that their kind is in danger.

Fed by fragmentary and often conflicting reports, sometimes by scientists who reveal their findings in defiance of orders to remain silent, our country is coming to a slow awareness that its environment is in harm's way. The people seem to sence, somehow, that this is to be *their* battle; that it will have to be fought with only marginal help, and that it may mean overcoming and reorienting industry, government, and often the two structured in concert. They seem to be intuitively rejecting the cover story and discovering the root truth that we are destroying nature under the steamroller of

progress; that we have arrived at the fourth quarter of the
game, and we are trailing.

The swelling chorus of concern could be heard throughout America as the decade of the '60s closed, and the politicians were listening. They began boarding the ecological
bandwagon in growing numbers, offering promises, plati-
tudes, and even legislation. One can only wonder if many of
these representatives are not reacting more to the heat than
to the light. So many seem to have been converted to the
legions of conservation in such haste, it has proven embarrassing. One highly placed science advisor descended on
Los Angeles recently to pronounce on the state of hydrocarbon smog. He promptly chided auto manufacturers to
"watch those *carbohydrates.*" As one impertinent wag
smirked: "Six months ago they couldn't *spell* ecology, and
now they lecture on it."

But whether the government leaders are worried about
the environment or merely re-election is probably unimportant. The fact is they appear to be willing at last to support
legislation aimed at improving our lot. They have been agon-
izingly slow in coming around, despite prodding by a
handful of legislators who have been aware of our deepening
problem.

One reason for the country's slow awakening has been
unwillingness of many scientists to speak out on the dangers
they are uniquely qualified to detect well in advance. This
reticence does not always spring from modesty; it frequently
results from being mired in the age-old swamp of conflicting
interests. A good many talented men of science are plying
their noble trade on behalf of government and industry. They

are moonlighting on study grants and contracts to supplement their often inadequate academic income. This is not at all illegal, but it does lead to a kind of professorial prostitution. They are straddling a splintery fence. When important issues arise that involve their corporate or governmental benefactors, these scientists refuse to talk, even when in possession of valuable information, for to do so would almost certainly dry up the fiscal flow. Several scientists have stated that the practice is widespread and growing.

To their credit, many of these scientists *want* to comment but cannot bring themselves to do so publicly. Sometimes, they will corner a reporter and deliver anonymous information and warnings they feel must be disseminated. One biochemist approached me in this manner last year. He felt compelled to comment — off the record — about the chemical pesticide strips commonly available in markets: "Those strips are taken home by people and are hung around the kitchen. They contain organic phosphate — one of the most toxic chemicals known to man. I believe if a child were to rub one of those strips and then lick his fingers, death might result." The chemist in question was working under a study contract from a chemical concern which manufactures such products. In another instance last year, I was granted an interview by the director of a science institution, but when I arrived to tape-record our conversation, five scientists were present and I was not permitted to identify which statement came from which scientist. Nerve in anonymous numbers.

The above, of course, is not intended to imply that the entire body of science is corrupt or running scared. On the contrary, there is a refreshing openness among most men who

work in the field today. Not nearly so many appear to be
concerned about possible damage to their "credentials" from
any public statement they might make. It has, in the past,
been a frustrating trait of these men that they would not
discuss a problem until they were dead certain of every fact
and detail. Today, they recognize that we cannot afford to
wait until all the returns are in when dealing with any matter
that might endanger society. Thus, subjects and findings
which stir controversy and disagreement in the world of
science are talked about openly. For instance, I found it very
difficult to find anyone willing to discuss the possibility of
pesticide damage to phytoplankton two years ago. Now it is
an open subject, although still controversial. There is little
question anymore that many top scientists, worried for years
about the trampling man is giving his planet, are now har-
boring even deeper fears and are even questioning whether we
can survive the destruction.

Airline pilots have an invisible marker known as the
point of no return. A variable meld of time, fuel, winds, and
distance, it is the precise position between point of departure
and destination beyond which the aircraft cannot return to
its base. Some scientists believe there is also a terminal
marker in the pollution of our environment, and if we go
beyond that point there will be no turning back – humanity
will be on the December side of its existence on earth. They
believe we are on a timetable for disaster.

It is a little difficult for most of us to accept, with a
straight face, the proposition that we may have painted ourselves into an ecological corner. It is preposterous on the face
of it. Are we not the ulitimate link in the chain, the highest

order in nature's scheme of things? Are we not the only member of the animal kingdom to have learned to speak and read and write? And to produce wondrous things such as atomic reactors and drive-in movies? Of course, and there's the hitch. Somewhere along the line, we forgot, in our conceit, that we *are* part of the environment. Unlike the lesser members of the ecological clan, we chose to shape our environment; to bulldoze it, concrete it, *bend* it to fit. We opted for a permanent-press world, and it didn't work. We are coming apart at the seams.

A growing number of scientists are questioning whether the earth's ecological web can hold together under the stress being put upon it by modern society. These men exhibit varying degress of alarm. A few believe we have blundered beyond our depth and are doomed already — trapped on the other side of the mirror and unable to come back. Ahead is a slow descent into oblivion. Others feel we have not missed our last chance, but may be approaching that point rapidly. One man in the latter camp is Doyle Grabarck, biochemist at the University of Maryland's Department of Physiology, and President of the North American Habitat Society.

Says Grabarck: "The problem of environmental contamination has become so great in magnitude that it is with justification that the majority of ecologists feel that we have passed the point when we could have reversed the degradative trend. I myself feel that we in the United States possess both the brain and money power to reverse the trend not only in this country, but on a world-wide basis. However, unless a dramatic and broad-scoped program is undertaken within the next five years, man's senseless destruction of his environment will inevitably lead to the termination of the human race."

Grabarck describes the ecology as a giant net. "If we pull a string loose, the whole thing unravels. In my opinion we are very close to pulling the string. If we do, I believe we will go in my lifetime. I'm twenty-seven."

Can it be — is it barely possible — these men are correct? They are in a better position to know than we, and there are disturbing signs supporting their position. On the northern coast of California, the sardines disappear. The crab catch off San Francisco drops by 80 percent over the last decade. Thousands of birds die mysteriously in Britain. The pelicans and other fish-eating birds appear to be heading straight for extinction. The crown of thorns starfish population takes an inexplicable surge. Coincidence? Or perhaps man's intervention with deadly poisons such as DDT? Whatever the cause, we are witnessing a massive disruption of the ecosystem.

All the above are obvious. What about the not so obvious — the subtle changes which we cannot yet detect, but which may be the seeds of disaster? As one scientist chillingly pointed out: "By the time we discover what is happening, we may well be twenty years too late."

If our elected officials believe even a part of what these men are saying, they are reacting to the crisis in puzzling fashion. For a nation drowning in its own waste, pennies are dribbled out to repair a few sewers — the equivalent of building the Aswan Dam with three beavers and a wad of chewing gum. Pushed to the wall with a mountain of evidence on DDT (available years ago), the government finally knuckles under to a partial phaseout of its use in the U.S. Since most of the DDT is exported — to return with the speed and regularity of an ocean liner — their action makes as much sense as taking birth pills 20 percent of the time.

If, as many believe, we are on a collision course with tragedy through pollution of our world, we may never have advance warning as to the approximate due date. Scientists explain that many items of information which would permit determination of our disaster deadline are missing. In some areas, research has burned up only vague indications — which in turn foster additional research. The scope is enormous, the scientific fields involved numerous. Even to seek an answer would require great expense and years of work. Yet, there are enough data to bring forth warnings of possible doom. Perhaps the best answer came from a botanist I questioned about the point of no return. He just gave me an odd look and shrugged: "When? We really cannot afford to find out."

Nature, in the final analysis, seems to have her own way of self-preservation. This writer, for one, believes that nature will balance herself in the end, and preserve life on earth — as she always has. She has shown a heartening capability of removing any threatening irritant. It just seems terribly unfortunate that the irritant, in this instance, is mankind.

Producer Don Widener and Jack Lemmon on the set of "The Slow
Guillotine."

The Slow Guillotine

On the following pages, the reader will find a verbatim
transcript of a one-hour television documentary, "The Slow
Guillotine," which prompted the writing of this book.

When presented May 10, 1969 on KNBC, the NBC-
owned television station for Los Angeles, "The Slow Guillotine" produced the greatest impact of any program in that
staion's history. NBC declined to present the program on the
full network because it was felt to be a local program about
one community's problems. An odd conclusion, inasmuch as
the program was filmed in New York, Michigan, Washington,
D.C.; Arizona, Nevada and California. The program was
eventually shown, however, on the five NBC-owned stations
in New York, Washington, D.C.; Chicago, Cleveland, and Los
Angeles.

The program proved that straightforward, honest films
can be produced and shown on television . . . to the benefit
of the public and to the credit of the television industry.
Alas, it is not always so. Many documentaries on controversial issues have all the driving force of a savage assault
by Flopsy, Mospsy, and Cottontail.

However, that is another subject for another time. The
transcript is printed here for the clear warning it contains,
and for those who will never see the film. Hopefully, the
words will move some to action . . . even without the superb
eloquence of Jack Lemmon, who appeared in and narrated
the program.

TRANSCRIPT OF
"THE SLOW GUILLOTINE"

JACK LEMMON: I'm Jack Lemmon. I am with you tonight because I am concerned; in fact I am just plain scared.
Before this program is over you probably will be too.

By luck or divine providence we have the only planet in our
solar system that can support life as we know it. It is the only
game in town. But for how long, that's what scares me.
Listen.

DR. RICHARD FELGER, CURATOR OF BOTANY, LOS
ANGELES MUSEUM OF NATURAL HISTORY: "Well, if
we don't come to our senses and do something in the way of
positive action soon, perhaps a half a century."

LOUIS FULLER, LOS ANGELES AIR POLLUTION CON-
TROL DISTRICT OFFICER: "It is my opinion that the
rate in which our atmosphere, our breathable air is being
contaminated is such that we don't have fifty years. I think
we will be very lucky if we have twenty-five years."

HAROLD KOENIG, PRESIDENT OF THE ECOLOGICAL
SCIENCE CORPORATION: "Well, I think we will find
that if no corrective actions are taken many of our urban
centers will be unliveable prior to the year 2000."

RALPH NADER, AUTHOR AND CRITIC: "I think that is
being generous."

JACK LEMMON: From around the world reports are
coming in, we are poisoning the sky. Clean water is only a

nostalgic childhood memory. In some mountain ranges whole forests are dying from air pollution. Many species of wild life are fighting a losing battle against extinction. Even the great oceans are beginning to lose the struggle against an avalanche of garbage from man, including pesticides and lead from automobile exhausts.

And while we count the dead and wounded millions among the wild life, nobody knows how badly man has been injured. What is most frightening, damn little is being done to avert what can be the greatest catastrophy of all time.

We are drifting, content for the most part, with occasional scientific warnings and flurries of activity; generally after the fact of tragedy. And faced with this stupendous problem we are trying to bail out the "Titanic" with a shot glass.

The program you are about to see concerns air pollution; however, smog is but one part of the problem. We are fouling our nest in a thousand other ways.

The situation is glum but it is not impossible, if we stop pussyfooting and start wildcatting.

Following its preliminary research a year ago KNBC felt the situation was so critical that something had to be done, and in a hurry. The station took an unprecedented step. It asked for and got the help of one of America's foremost scientists.

A research program began on a crash basis with one goal: find a way to reduce automotive smog, the chief villain of air pollution; and tonight the hopeful results of that project will be presented.

For years smog has always been a favorite gag for TV comics. They could always count on it for laughs. Tourists sent home bottles of smoke labelled "Los Angeles Smog." Everybody was laughing, when they weren't coughing.

If you are still laughing about pollution, listen to four experts from four different fields.

DR. FELGER: "In pesticide pollution alone, our own national symbol is very rapidly becoming extinct. I think that first we must back up here and realize that extinction means that a form of life is gone forever and no amount of technology, no amount of money . . . it is not possible to bring that kind of life back again; it is gone with a finality.

"One of the countless examples of extinction because of pollution is our own national symbol, the bald eagle. Each year the eggs become thinner and thinner, and now the eggs break before they hatch; that is the end of the life cycle. We are living organisms and man has been modifying his environment — and not only his environment, the environment of all life. And now this modification is so serious that it threatens life, many kinds of life, with extinction — including man."

HAROLD KOENIG   "Smog is a very fundamental cause of the rise in the average mean temperature of the earth, which in recent years has come up a half degree. And this is significant because it begins to affect the polar masses and you could well within the foreseeable future have tremendous tragedies: hundreds and thousands of people wiped off this earth as a result of melting polar ice masses. As an example, the smog precludes the historical radiation that nature provided in the ecological balance that was given with this earth.

"If no corrective actions are taken, many of our urban centers will be unliveable prior to the year 2000. Unliveable in terms of human beings, animal life, vegatation . . . any living organism."

LOUIS FULLER: "I think you are optimistic on a half a century; you are talking fifty years from now we will be in trouble? No, I think we are in trouble now, and there is a possibility we may have gone beyond the point where we can reverse.

"I am not trying to be dramatic, I am trying to tell you that in my opinion, based upon everything that I have known in this field, and I have talked to scientists from all over the world including the Soviet Union, which has had their scientists visit us here, it is my opinion that the rate at which our atmosphere, our breathable air, is being contaminated is such that we do not have fifty years. I think we will be very lucky if we have twenty-five."

RALPH NADER: "I think that is being generous. I think there may be other problems of pollution developing in the next few years that can be even more serious than the traditional hydrocarbons and nitrogen oxides.

"For example, there are two sources of vehicle pollution that have not even begun to be studied hardly; asbestos from grinding and wearing of brake linings for example, and the grinding of rubber tires and the particulate manner that gets into our lungs and bodies."

JACK LEMMON: It doesn't take a detective to find evidence to support these predictions. There is chilling proof at

Lake Arrowhead, a resort five thousand feet above the Los
Angeles-Riverside Basin. On days when the smog builds up
below in the valley, the first gray tentacles can be seen at
dawn, slithering into the foothills.

Two-thirds of the stately old Ponderosa pines are dead or
doomed. Some of these trees were here when Washington
quartered at Valley Forge. When one is damaged by smog,
death always comes, usually within ten years.

Most people here seem unconcerned; either they don't know
or they ignore the fact that air pollution has invaded their
paradise with disastrous consequences. Understandably,
people who depend on scenic beauty for a livelihood are
unhappy about any talk of smog and dying trees.

One developer threatened to sue NBC if this program told of
Arrowhead trees being killed by pollution. *Timberline
Journal* publisher Dick Stewart has tried to arouse public
awareness.

DICK STEWART, PUBLISHER, THE TIMBERLINE
JOURNAL, LAKE ARROWHEAD: "My father-in-law
moved up here in 1923, and the family still has about two
hundred acres up here; so we're interested not only as property owners, but also as a newspaper editor.

"About seven years ago we noticed that we were losing a lot
of trees to the smog; so in consultation with our forest ranger
up here, Tom Neff, we started planting Sequoia Gigantia,
which, we understand, is not as susceptible as the native trees
up here; and although we haven't had good luck with them,
we're still planting. We've some now about twelve feet tall,

and it seems to us as though the people in the community aren't taking this as seriously as they should. But we're trying to do all we can.

"About six months ago we printed a large article that was put out by the U.S. Forest Service, calling to their attention the fact that the smog was going to be destroying our forest here probably in another twenty to fifty years. And even though that doesn't concern us personally, as landowners we feel that we should pass the land on better than we got it."

JACK LEMMON: To millions of Southern Californians, these mountains are a happy playground. But the fun-filled activities are strangely like a carnival in a graveyard to one man, Dr. Paul Miller, plant pathologist for the U.S. Forest Service.

DR. PAUL MILLER, PLANT PATHOLOGIST, U.S. FOREST SERVICE: "Month after month we watch these trees die. We know that the only way to stop the dying is to stop the smog. We've tried everything we know to treat the trees to prevent them from dying. Nothing has worked. The needles fall from the trees as a result of injury brought upon them by the oxidant in smog. The oxidant literally destroys the tissue inside the needle. The tissue dies and the needle falls off.

"These are the needles from a healthy Ponderosa pine. These needles have been hit by smog. These needles are little factories which produce the sugars to sustain the life of the tree. When these are gone, the tree has no food reserve and it dies. I feel more like a plant mortician than a plant pathologist."

JACK LEMMON: Dr. Miller is one of the team of scientists studying air pollution in laboratories at the University of California at Riverside. Here, specialists observe the effect of smog on plants and try to devise defenses against various pollutants. Finding the exact chemical make-up of smog is the job of Doctor Edgar R. Stevens.

DR. EDGAR R. STEVENS, UNIVERSITY OF CALIFOR-NIA AT RIVERSIDE: "This is an apparatus we use for studying the conversion of the relatively harmless things that come from auto exhausts into the harmful products which make smog. Some of these are hydrocarbons, and we also have nitric oxide. Under the influence of the blue light which you saw, and which we use for artificial sunlight, this is converted to another compound which we can show you. This tube contains nitric oxide, the syringe contains air. When I mix the two you will see a reddish brown color which you often see in the Los Angeles atmosphere. See the color developing quite rapidly? In the natural outdoor atmosphere this requires not only nitric oxide and air but also sunlight and hydrocarbon."

JACK LEMMON: Farm owners are taking financial body blows from smog. Perhaps the hardest hit have been the lettuce growers, who have generally given up battling the problem in the Los Angeles-Riverside area. They now operate in cleaner areas outside Los Angeles.

DR. O. CLIFTON TAYLOR, UNIVERSITY OF CALIFOR-NIA AT RIVERSIDE: "That is the kind of damage, Judy, that causes an awful lot of loss of crops in Southern California. Injuries such as that can be disastrous to the farmer. I have seen as much as seventy or eighty acres of lettuce damaged like that that had to be plowed up, and a complete loss. If it does not get that serious, sometimes the farmer can salvage part of his crop and can market it with just some injury to the leaves; but most of the time it's a complete loss.

"The damage really runs into the millions in Southern California and the grower has to be somewhat of a gambler to be able to stay in the business."

JACK LEMMON: Doctor Seymour Calvert, director of the research staff here, estimates total plant loss at two hundred and forty million dollars or more annually.

DR. SEYMOUR CALVERT, DIRECTOR, RESEARCH STAFF: "This is our small-particle laboratory where we do work on devices and methods for determining what's in the air, and also on various devices for removing particles, dust, mists and so forth from industrial exhaust gases. These are part of the total mix of capabilities we need in order to know what's in the air, what it does, how it gets there, and what we can do about keeping it out of the air.

"Now as far as photochemical smog goes we know quite a bit about what it is, about the kind of harm it does. We have a pretty good idea of how it gets there, but we don't know too precisely what to do about it."

JACK LEMMON: Although we know the effect of air pollution on plants, nobody is sure about the consequence to humans. We cannot isolate man for testing. The alternate: animals.

Doctor Arthur Gregory, specialist in animal physiology, works with spider monkeys. Kept in separate cages under controlled environments, the monkeys in clean-air cages are given food also grown in clean air. The unlucky fellows in the other cage get the same dirty air and food as you and I. On smoggy days the monkeys in ordinary air get red eyes, just as you and I.

To the practiced eye of our reporters, it did seem that the clean-air monkeys had longer and more glamorous tails. Dr. Gregory declined to comment, except to note his principal investigation involved the other end.

The study of mice has shown something more grim: male mice die sooner in smog.

DR. OTIS EMIK, UNIVERSITY OF CALIFORNIA AT RIVERSIDE: "The spontaneous activity of mice has been very significantly reduced by exposure to the Los Angeles-type smog. When we took ten mice and exposed them for thirteen months, here at Riverside, we found they ran slower when the smog level was up."

JACK LEMMON: Whatever we do is more difficult in smog. The gloomy possibility is that humans as well as mice are growing older, faster.

Dr. Emik's results with mice overlap the findings from a six-year study of the performance of the track team at San Marino, California, High School.

JACK BRADFORD, COACH, SAN MARINO HIGH SCHOOL: "One of the runners that was running on my team back in 1958's father was very interested in air pollution research and recommended to the U.S. Public Health

Service that they might be able to find records over the years
on how the boys did under smoggy conditions during our
regular running season.

"We found that in most of the meets where there was a high
incidence of oxidants on the day we were competing, the
boys would usually perform about ten to twenty seconds
below what the expectancy for that particular day would be.
It seems to affect all age levels identically; even our boys who
have been in open competition and in big invitational meets
are affected identically with the young fourteen-year olds."

JACK LEMMON: Mice age faster, a track team's performance is down, lettuce fields are wiped out, trees die by the
thousands . . . they all have one thing in common: they were
healthy in the beginning.

Patients at the emphysema ward of Olive View Hospital in
the San Fernando Valley don't have that plus going for them.
When smog is an annoyance to some of us, it becomes an
episode of pure terror here.

DR. ROMAN YANDA, OLIVE VIEW HOSPITAL: "Smog
has crept into all areas of our life. We, in studying this problem, have found that there is smog in medical oxygen. This is
true when the oxygen from liquid air is in an area where the
fuel plants are, or industry is; the air cannot be clean and
there must be smog in it.

"Measuring the level of hydrocarbon in the air in Los
Angeles, we found an average level of two parts per million.
When we measured the level of hydrocarbon in medical
oxygen — five samples from five different companies — we
found levels ranging from fourteen to twenty-eight parts per

million. This is many times more than the level we breathe in.
And who gets that oxygen? The sickest of the people, the
ones who need the cleanest air, do not get it. And because it
does not bother us, the healthy ones, we pay no attention to
it. Do we have to get ill first before we do something about
this, or can we start taking preventive measures?"

JACK LEMMON: Many who can find work in a less polluted environment leave Los Angeles.

LEONARD PARSONS, WORKER, LEAR COMPANY:
"My name is Leonard Parsons, and my wife and I moved
away from Los Angeles last year here to Reno to avoid the
severe smog problem. We love Los Angeles very much, but we
couldn't put up with the smog. My friend Chuck Zimmerman
also left Los Angeles."

CHUCK ZIMMERMAN, WORKER, LEAR COMPANY:
"My doctor told me to move out for the same reason — due
to the smog. My wife had a lump in her throat, and we
moved up here; the lump disappeared and my wife feels very
fine now."

JACK LEMMON: For those like young Larry Green, who
stay in smoggy areas, there are rules laid down by the family
physicians, including no smoking and no outdoor exercise.

Doctors now take air pollution seriously and more are beginning to speak out on the subject.

DR. ARTHUR GROSSMAN, PEDIATRICIAN: "We think
that the repeated insults to the respiratory tract, for instance,
the sulphuric acid and the nitric oxides which can produce

nitric acid, can interfere with the enzyme systems of the respiratory tract.

"The strongest enzyme which is for the benefit of the human being is the lysozyme, which finds its way from the lacrimal gland into the nose, into the respiratory tract, and all the way down to the top of the bronchial tubes; and any chemical in the atmosphere which could slow, destroy, or inactivate that enzyme will produce chronic respiratory disease.

"There is a great deal of research now to show that not only is the enzyme inactivated or possibly destroyed, but that a new type of protein appears in the tears, and this protein itself is irritating and produces the symptoms of the smog syndrome.

"We know that many people complain of burning eyes, dry throats, runny noses, shortness of breath. The shortness of breath is a very important problem in the adolescent age group because we fear that the cumulative effect of this retrosternal difficulty will show up in the next generation."

JACK LEMMON: There is a growing belief among scientists that the exotic products of man's technology are more advanced than his knowledge of their effects and control.

DDT was originally hailed as a great advance. It is now a dread pollutant around the world. Carried in rains and through ocean currents, long-lasting pesticides can be found even in the Antarctic.

A new and serious pollution is lead from the automobile fumes and lead smelters. The amount of lead pouring into our water in the past twenty years has increased dramatically. Lead is highly toxic and it's absorbed into the bones and

tissues of our bodies; it even interferes with the central
nervous system. Lead, pesticides and more have become
common commodities in air and water.

HAROLD KOENIG: "I don't drink this water and neither
should you. I don't trust the quality of this water in terms of
the pollutants that I know could well exist; not because it is
Washington D.C., but because it's typical of the water in
most of the urbanized areas of this country.

"As you look out here and see the Potomac River, you can
see how the reservoir, this receiving body of water, can digest
the pesticides and the various contaminants that are being fed
into that historical body of water. And as you look out, you
begin to see the other problems of pollution.

"You see the trail of the kerosene particulate out of the jet
planes taking off from National Airport. You see the various
particulate emissions coming out of the process plants, out of
the thermal generating power plants just across the Potomac.
You see the elements of smog that are beginning to relate
right here in Washington D.C. as they have done so terribly in
the Los Angeles Basin."

JACK LEMMON: Contrary to popular opinion, Los
Angeles is not the smog capital of the world. Several cities are
in worse shape from air pollution, and others can look for-
ward to making this list as population, traffic, and industry
increase. We will visit one of the newest victims in a moment.

This is one of the most popular resort cities in America, it
attracts winter visitors like a magnet. Many have stayed on to
transfer their business operations here; more people, more
cars, more industry.

Five years ago it was a bad day when you couldn't see sixty
miles. That was five years ago. This is Phoenix, Arizona,
today, in the Valley of the Sun. The natives will tell you
there now seems to be a lot more valley than sun. State pollution officials blame cars as the cause of eighty-five percent of
the Phoenix smog. Smelters get credit for the rest.

Whatever the source, it is here and it's bad.

Officials suspect the area has already suffered damage to
plants and trees. The residents seem bewildered; few thought
that it could happen here.

This home on the range has heard a discouraging word!

New York is the most populous city in the country. Among
other things it has the tallest building, Broadway and the
Statue of Liberty; it has Wall Street, Times Square, the Mets;
and it has Central Park.

And it has one more thing: the filthiest air in the United
States.

This of course can only be one place in the air pollution
picture, mother lode — Los Angeles. This is smog's home-
town. It started here in the 1940s. The industries, the people,
and even the cars will never be the same because of it.

Los Angeles is sort of the "university of smog." Other afflicted cities send representatives here to find out how
Angelenos manage to keep breathing, because Los Angeles
has had it all.

Today the city has the tightest smog controls in the country;
still . . . the aerial cesspool hangs on, and grows.

The man who rides shotgun on L.A.'s pollution patrol is its
hard-nosed smog chief, Louis Fuller.

LOUIS FULLER, LOS ANGELES SMOG CHIEF: "There
could be a major disaster and a loss of life as a result of air
pollution from motor vehicles in this area. In Los Angeles
County we have very, very strict controls over industry. As a
matter of fact we can close down industry. Within a matter
of seconds we can start the shut-down procedures, and these
plans are already on file and implemented. Industry is connected with our control center by radio so that it is a matter
of pushing buttons and we start the shut-down.

"But we do not have this type of control over four million
vehicles. And as far as the authority which appears in one
piece of legislation that I have the authority to shut down
motor vehicle traffic . . . well, good luck! I haven't got a
chance!"

JACK LEMMON: Ralph Nader agrees about a possible
smog disaster.

RALPH NADER: "A quick climatic change can come on so
fast that it could cause a disaster something on the order of
the London and Donora episodes. Whether or not it causes a
disaster, it's quite clear that growing medical opinion is that
people who have respiratory diseases shouldn't live in the Los
Angeles area. Isn't that a savage commentary?"

JACK LEMMON: The desperate search for clean air has led
to some very fancy blue-sky theories over the years. One
fellow wanted to bore enormous holes in the mountains, you
see, so that the smog could get into the desert. The problem

being that the smog already goes over the mountains at ten thousand feet or more; gets into the desert on its own!

Another fellow wanted to build devices all along the freeways that would suck in the smog, till some pessimist said "suck it where?"

Another fellow wanted all the Los Angelenos to breath in at the same time and then blow out at the same time till you turn blue. Neighboring towns threatened to blow back; that was the end of that.

But on the serious side, others look to new means of energy to power automobiles. One has given up. General Electric told KNBC's reporter that it will not produce an electric car because the battery has simply not progressed to the point where an electric car is feasible or practical for the family. But when one quits another begins.

Reno, Nevada is a city tailored to high rollers, but even Reno doesn't see many men willing to lay ten million dollars on the line. One fellow who likes a long shot hunch is doing just that. He is William Lear, president of Lear Motors, who is betting it all on a revolutionary steam-driven car he is building with the help of famed designer Ken Wallis. We asked Mr. Lear what effect it would have on air pollution.

WILLIAM LEAR, PRESIDENT, LEAR MOTORS: "Well, we think it will eliminate air pollution as we now see it, but of course it will take some time because it will probably take six to ten years before we get the present cars off the road before you can see the effect of a car that reduces the present pollution of the present automobiles to one percent of what it is.

"We intend to go into mass production on the engines and we intend to make a limousine and a mass-produced car that will sell for in the six to seven thousand-dollar class. This is the engine, and this engine will be the engine that will be used in a car the size of, let us say, an Oldsmobile or a Buick or even a Cadillac, and they will develop three hundred horsepower in a car, lets say of an Oldsmobile Eighty-Eight, and it will bring it up to ninety miles an hour in a quarter of a mile, and will have a top speed of one hundred thirty miles an hour, and will burn less fuel than a standard gasoline car by about twenty percent.

"We believe that the burning of fuel, regardless of the kind of fuel it is, it is terribly important to get it all burned; and in the internal combustion engine it has such a very, very short period of time that it has to burn, and it has to burn under such high pressures that it develops the noxious and the nitrous oxides and the hydrocarbons and so forth that fill the atmosphere and cause smog.

"As a matter of fact, I think in ten years the internal combustion engine will only be seen in The Smithsonian Institute."

JACK LEMMON: Ken Wallis removes the protecting covering to give you the first public look at a mock-up of Lear's new motor. It's installed in a 1966 Oldsmobile for test by the California Highway Patrol.

KEN WALLIS: "The whole principle of the thing is different. In the place of the normal transmission, down below here, we have a small steam motor powered by a steam generator, shown here, and an auxiliary package here, which constantly provides all the accessory power to support both the steam power plant and the services required by the vehicle."

JACK LEMMON: General Motors is also investigating steam power, along with its G.M. sterling engine electric hybrid car. This experimental vehicle is designed to explore the use of a low-emmission engine with an electric drive system for a small car.

At Ford the chips are being placed on a turbine engine as the power plant of the future. Although Ford, too, is looking into the steam motor idea.

Engineers at Ford say drivers vie for their turn at the wheel of this big turbine truck. Its pollution rate is higher than steam but it is the cost factor that keeps gas turbine engines off the roads. Ford says that it will be overcome within a few years.

Motor vehicles – the bane and blessing of mankind. They have increased his productivity; they have raised his living standard; they have broadened his horizons; they have served him in a thousand other ways. They have also taught him a few new cuss words; they have shattered his serenity, and they have dirtied his air.

With the first motor vehicles came the first smog. It was a package deal!

Detroit is a city geared to an industry under fire. The auto manufacturers, troubled in recent times over safety devices, have a bigger problem now in pollution. The first rumbles came in the early 1950s from an eye-smarting Los Angeles. Detroit's first reaction was to point the finger at others.

Complaints against the auto makers have grown in sound and ferocity ever since.

Early this year, following a federal grand jury investigation, the U.S. Justice Department filed suit, charging deliberate delay in development of effective antismog devices for cars.

Producer Don Widener interviewed executives of the auto companies just hours before the Justice Department acted. In the test facility at General Motors he talked with Dr. Fred Bowditch.

DR. FRED BOWDITCH: "We are running both California and federal standard exhaust tests on hydrocarbons, carbon monoxide, and oxides of nitrogen. We have just recently finalized the test procedures so that we can tell what our oxides of nitrogen levels are from our vehicles, and we are presently going through the process of determining just where we stand right now, and what some of our initial ideas in control measures can do for oxides of nitrogen."

DON WIDENER: "This date for these restrictions is not very far away; do you think that you can make it?"

DR. FRED BOWDITCH: "We sure hope so. We certainly intend to. We think probably we can. To be very accurate about it, we don't really know to date."

DON WIDENER: "Doctor, how do you plan to approach it, is it going to be a tack-on device, or will you modify the engine; how do you plan to attack it?"

DR. BOWDITCH: "Well, I wish I really knew all the answers, Don. Certainly in some instances it will be both. We may well be able to have engine modification in some areas. It could well be that it may eventually require some kind of tack-on devices. Honestly, today we just don't know. There are both kinds of approaches to the problem, certainly."

DON WIDENER: "Dr. Bowditch, in California oxides of nitrogen are generally thought of as a pretty undesireable product. You have an opinion that differs from that?"

DR. BOWDITCH: "Well, we do have an honest technical difference of opinion with some of our other associates in the technical field of atmospheric pollution. Our own smog-chamber results appear to indicate that from where the L.A. atomosphere is today, a reduction of automotive oxides of nitrogen may actually increase the photochemical smog situation in Los Angeles."

DON WIDENER: "We understand that when the industry began to reduce hydrocarbons in the automotive engine they got an increase in oxides, is this correct?"

CHARLES HEINAN, CHRYSLER CORPORATION: "Yes, in all probability. My estimate is something in the order of fifteen percent. As a matter of fact, I have charted it up here. This is a series of charts that I keep for my own education, and they show the effect of various possible events, or existing events.

"Now, here is the oxides of nitrogen chart. You will notice that the increase was going up-tonnage over here, approximately in proportion to miles driven; and it would be a straight line along here.

"Then at this point we started putting in devices, and I have shown a rise which corresponds to my estimate of what that rise is. Then we get up to the point here where the California standards start being considered; this would be 1971, and if the standards are passed and we put on the necessary hardware, this is the way that line will go."

DON WIDENER: "Now these standards in '71: they are in California, they are not in the nation. Do you think you can meet those standards in '71?"

CHARLES HEINAN: "We have every reason to believe that we are going to meet them. If they become law we will meet them."

JACK LEMMON: Ford engineer Bob Campau described research being conducted on a catalyst muffler.

BOB CAMPAU: "On this car here we have assembled several of the hardware and fuel components that we believe are necessary to develop a virtually emmission-free vehicle. The chief components are this catalytic converter here, designed to reduce the oxides of nitrogen, and following that, another catalytic converter designed to reduce the hydrocarbons and carbon monoxide. Both of these converters operate off of what we call a logic system, which senses the vehicle's operating speed and operating condition of the vehicle and brings the gases through the converters during urban driving regimes, and bypasses the converters on turnpike driving conditions for long periods of time."

DON WIDENER: "Why is it necessary to bypass here?"

BOB CAMPAU: "Well, we are bypassing to extend the life of the catalysts that we are working with. There are two things that seriously affect the life of a catalyst and one of them is high temperature glazing of the catalyst surface itself. It destroys the activity of the catalyst. The second one is the presence of tetraethyl lead in the gasoline. In this car the gasoline has been modified to eliminate the tetraethyl lead; we are also trying to eliminate the high temperature glazing that would occur if the car was running down the turnpike for several hours, three or four hours."

DON WIDENER: "Do you think then that they will have to change the fuel as well as the muffler?"

BOB CAMPAU: "Right. In our program we are taking a systems approach. We are modifying the fuel where needed; we are modifying the vehicle where it is needed to reach these levels that we are shooting for."

DON WIDENER: "Now, what are your dates on this? Obviously, this is not going to be ready for the 1971 standards in California for oxides?"

BOB CAMPAU: "Right, we are working on much more advanced systems, systems that would probably be needed in let's say ten years . . . that can be ready for production in about ten years."

JACK LEMMON: There is little doubt that auto makers are placing more emphasis on smog abatement today. We tried to determine exactly how much money is being allocated for that purpose.

DR. BOWDITCH: "I don't think we can really give you a good figure for this, Don. It's certainly in the millions, but I'm afraid I just am not able to give you a number. I simply don't know."

CHARLES HEINAN: "That's a very hard figure to give you. It's in the millions. The reason it's a hard figure is that at one time or other, thousands of people are involved, part time or full time. But it's definitely in the millions."

RALPH NADER: "General Motors produces more than half of the vehicles in this country. If you take the vehicles it produces and the plants that it operates, it contributes thirty-five percent of all the air pollution in this nation by tonnage. At the same time, General Motors is spending two hundred fifty million dollars in the past year or two to change its image in terms of its brand name, so you see 'G.M. The Mark of Excellence' on its dealers and on its products.

"It is spending less than ten million dollars in advanced research and development to clean up that lethal, infernal, internal combustion engine.

"Until the company can be personalized in terms of its own chief executives, until for example, the people of Los Angeles can require these executives to come and meet the people; to be exposed to their cries of anguish and their pain; to survey the area of their depredations, then General Motors is not going to move because basically there is no penalty for inaction and delay. And, if senators and presidential candidates and governors have to go and meet the people and discuss the issues with them, I see no reason why corporate executives shouldn't be required to do the same thing."

JACK LEMMON: Tougher state standards for automotive emissions will become effective in California in 1971. We asked government and civic leaders what if the auto manufacturers fail to meet these standards.

LOUIS FULLER: "Well they just are not going to sell any automobiles in California if I can prevent it. Now, if this sounds like a rather strong statement, when I say 'I', I'm talking about the State of California . . . the Legislature . . . our elected officials.

"If they cannot control the tons of poison which is being discharged into our liveable atmosphere, then they are just going to have to stop producing this type of automobile, and the sale of such devices should be prohibited, by law. And it's just that simple. Either you cure it, or you don't sell it."

KENNETH HAHN, LOS ANGELES COUNTY SUPER- VISOR: "Well, I'll ask for another federal grand jury to be convened to find out why."

RALPH NADER: "The question is, Suppose they don't? What happens?

"Nothing! There are no strict penalties, there is no will in the executive branch in Washington or in California to really get tough."

SENATOR GEORGE MURPHY: "First of all, in any federal legislation we can't make the standards go beyond the capabilities of the engineers. When we drew these standards in California, we thought, we believed, that the automotive manufacturers can meet these standards, and I am quite certain they will. Now in the event that we find that the standards are too high, that they are not feasible, or practical, or possible, naturally then you would have to make some adjustments."

JACK LEMMON: Ralph Nader offered his own plan to stimulate action on the smog problem.

RALPH NADER: "First of all, personal confrontation between people in the smog areas and top executives of the auto companies, in public forums. Second, pressure on auto dealers, who in turn will feed back this pressure to their companies. Third, tough criminal and civil penalties for violation of these standards. And fourth, the development by government of research and development funds for innovation, for the kind of development that will get rid of the internal combustion engine and give us a vehicle that does not pollute the air. The same kind of government-inspired innovation should hold true for industrial pollution as well."

JACK LEMMON: Senator George Murphy of California is an optimist. Despite the statistical signposts which indicate mounting trouble from pollution, he believes answers can and will be found as time goes by.

SENATOR MURPHY: "Well, I sometimes wonder whether these facts are true. I hate to find myself in disagreement with the scientists, because over the years I have found they have been pretty right. And I know that they have had some frightful stories of what is going to happen if we don't clean up that air.

"I do also know that from time to time as man goes along and progresses, he finds answers to these problems, and I'm kind of a hopeful fellow, and I think maybe we will find the answer to this one too, as we go along. We are not going to give up a great town like Los Angeles . . . not even to smog!

"One of the things that disturbs me is the fact that the federal government and the state governments let these things get so far out of hand before they started to really worry about them. For instance, right down the street here the Potomac River, they have a joke you know; they say you don't water ski there because if you fall in, by the time they get you out things are growing out of your ears. Now that's how bad the Potomac is."

JACK LEMMON: Not all smog programs are big or governmental. A small private laboratory in Monrovia, California, may hold the solution to our major source of smog: the family auto. And we'll be back with that report in just a minute.

Early last year KNBC decided that a local, independent effort might help find a solution to smog; and where better to try than Los Angeles, with its abundance of smog and scientific talent.

A meeting was arranged with noted scientist Milton Farber, NBC vice-president Robert T. Howard, and producer Don Widener — friend and former colleague of Farber.

Farber, a key member of the team which developed the first atomic bomb, agreed to "explore the possibility." The initial formula was written the same afternoon in a Burbank restaurant. Six months later, "possibility" had become "probability."

Assisting Farber is a team of senior scientists, including Doctor Sigmund Harris, another key man on the first atomic bomb project.

Tonight a revolutionary new double-chambered catalyst muffler exists, with a strong chance it can virtually eliminate automotive exhaust pollution.

MILTON FARBER, PRESIDENT, ANTIPOL CORPORA-TION: "We were approached by people in this area — in the California area — very much interested in solving the automobile exhaust problem, and a new corporation was set up called the Anti-Pollution Corporation of America, Antipol for short . . . privately financed. This corporation has funded a project here at this laboratory to build an antismog muffler which would not only remove the nitrogen oxide pollutants but at the same time would also remove the other two main ingredients, carbon monoxide and hydrocarbons.

"Nitrogen oxide is produced at high temperatures in the engine and it's one of the facts of nature that it is an ir-reversible process. In other words, when you cool off the high temperature exhaust the nitrogen oxide doesn't go back to nitrogen and oxygen. Instead, it stays as nitrogen oxide.

"However, if you pass the nitrogen oxide over a suitable catalyst, this will aid in providing the proper thermo-dynamics, which means that it will reduce back to nitrogen and oxygen. One of the ingredients formed in the exhaust is carbon monoxide, and this helps the reduction, and nitrogen oxide in conjunction with carbon monoxide on a catalyst can be readily reduced to nitrogen and carbon dioxide, which are harmless ingredients.

"It's what we call a dual catalyst device. We have first stage for the reduction, which we call reduction catalyst, for re-duction of the nitrogen oxides. After the gas leaves the first stage, reducing the nitrogen oxide content, air injection takes place and it enters the catalytic second stage, in which the hydrocarbons and CO are oxidized. So it's a reduction and oxidation-type device for the three pollutants.

"I think we ought to be able to have a fairly suitable device on cars within a few months, maybe a few of these on state cars, possibly as many as ten, and have them undergo a year's testing.

"The first device, we hope, will be a year device — one that will remove pollutants to state levels for a year."

DON WIDENER: "Is there anything in the development of a catalyst muffler that could not have been done twenty-five or thirty years ago?"

MILTON FARBER: "Probably not. Scientifically, the straightforward chemical reactions taking place, the thermodynamic reactions, are well known, have been well known for many years, and if somebody wanted to do it then, he could have done it then as well as now."

JACK LEMMON: At a scientific conference held just last month it was revealed that there are no baby pelicans along the Southern Californian coast this year. Pesticides have made the egg shells so thin they break before they hatch. It's the same with most birds of prey. Pollution has reached the point where there is little left to contaminate. It's now just a matter of degree. How much can we tolerate and still survive?

And don't be misled by the fact that pollution doesn't kill with dramatic suddenness. Fatal is fatal, whether you are conked with a rock or you are nibbled to death by a duck!

Science, engineering, government, and industry seem more intent on intramural bickering than cooperation; and yet these elements must work together in harmony if we are going to salvage the country from the mess that some feel is already irreversible.

It sounds hokey, but you — the individual citizen — you are the only guy with a solution. You alone hold the power to move government and industry.

Now we have shown you tonight how your resources are being plundered year after year after year after year, and this while the government talks of studies to determine "criteria" and "levels of tolerance."

Science keeps trying to devise a tree that will grow in polluted air. Now, for crying out loud, why do we have to put up with that?! And meanwhile, back at the factory, industry pleads for tolerance because purification equipment costs money.

Well it's enough!

Now, write to your congressman, the governor, or the mayor, and don't ask; *demand* action! Tell them what you saw on this program and if you get a form letter back, send a copy to his political opponent and keep one for yourself. You should know his name on election day.

And, if you don't take over, pollution will; because at this point, it looks very much like Chicken Little was right.

Suggested Readings

Problems of Combined Sewer Facilities and Overflows 1967, U.S. Department of the Interior, Federal Water Pollution Control Administration WP-20-11

Air Pollution and Health, Published by the National Tuberculosis Association, 1740 Broadway, New York, New York 10019

Lake Erie Report: A Plan for Water Pollution Control, August 1968, U.S. Department of the Interior, Federal Water Pollution Control Administration, Great Lakes Region

Biological Problems in Water Pollution, Third Seminar, 1962, U.S. Department of Health, Education and Welfare, Public Health Service

Community Action Program for Water Pollution Control, National Association for Counties/Research Division

Environmental Impact of The Big Cypress Swamp Jetport, U.S. Department of the Interior, September, 1969

Law and Contempory Problems: Air Pollution Control, Duke University Law Review, Vol. XXXIII, Spring, 1968, No. 2

Marine Science Affairs — A Year of Broadened Participation, Third Report of the President to the Congress on Marine Resources and Engineering Development, January, 1969

Our Nation and the Sea: A Plan for National Action, Report of the Commission on Marine Science, Engineering and Resources

Pesticide — Wildlife Studies by States, Provinces and Universities, Fish and Wildlife Service Circular 224, May 1965

Toxic Substances and Ecological Cycles, by G. M. Woodwell, Reprinted from *Scientific American,* March 1967, Published by W. H. Freeman and Company

CREDITS

The photographs in this volume are reproduced by kind permission of the following publications, governmental departments, and photographers:

Chicago Tribune, page 60
Dallas Morning News, page 60
Louisville Times, pages 65, 86
Los Angeles Pollution Control District, pages 46, 47, 58, 68
Stan Moore, Leigh Wiener Photography, pages facing Foreword, and 244
National Air Pollution Control Administration, pages 43, 58, 101
Darrell Salk, page 11
Statewide Air Pollution Research Center — University of
    California; Riverside, California; page 84
U.S. Department of Agriculture, Forest Service, page 80
U.S. Department of the Interior, Photographer: Cecil W.
    Stoughton, page 183
U.S. Department of the Interior National Park Service,
    Photographer: Jack E. Boucher, pages 193, 209
U.S. Department of the Interior National Park Service,
    Photographer: Ernst T. Christenson, page 184
U.S. Department of the Interior National Park Service,
    Photographer: Arthur F. Fawcett, page 36
U.S. Department of the Interior National Park Service,
    Photographer: M. Woodbridge Williams, pages 183, 184, 187,
    188, 195, 196, 198, 200, 201
Don Widener, pages 18, 75, 105, 169, 225, 234

The Conrad Cartoon is reprinted by permission of the
    Register and Tribune Syndicate.

The Karl Hubenthal Cartoon is reprinted by permission of
    the *L.A. Herald-Examiner.*

The charts in "Running Scared," which show the decline of
the sardine fisheries, were graciously provided by
Walter Thomsen of the California Department of Fish and Game.

Timetable for Disaster
The text of this book was designed by Kay McRee and typeset by Creative Ad Typographers, Van Nuys, California, in 12-point Aldine Roman on their IBM Magnetic Tape "Selectric" Composer. The headings and display type were set in Eurostile bold condensed by Continental Graphics, a division of Republic Corporation, Los Angeles, California. The printing was done by offset lithography by Stecher-Traung-Schmidt Corporation, San Francisco, California, and the paper is 60# Simpson Lee vellum finish. The book was bound by The Cardoza Bookbinding Company, San Francisco, California, in Holliston Mills' Sturdetan Pyroxylin coated kraft paper, matte finish. The jacket was designed by Gerry Rosentswieg, The Graphics Studio, Los Angeles, California.